Small Motor Cruisers

Small Motor Cruisers

Nigel Warren

Drawings by Beryl Riches

Adlard Coles Limited   London

Granada Publishing Limited
First published in Great Britain by Adlard Coles Limited
Frogmore St Albans Hertfordshire AL2 2NF and
3 Upper James Street London W1R 4BP

ISBN 0 229 11537 3

Printed in Great Britain by
William Clowes & Sons, Limited
London, Beccles and Colchester

Contents

Foreword

This is a book solely about small motor boats. And it is not a glorified glossy brochure tempting you to buy a gleaming power cruiser shown streaking across blue sunlit waters. It is, I hope, a practical guide to the various types of motor boat that one can buy bearing in mind the realities of owning a boat, particularly in Britain. The tides and unpredictable weather around our coast demand a seaworthy, reliably engined and properly equipped boat, while inland our shallow and obstacle-ridden canals demand a tough and specially shaped craft.

Whether you are thinking of buying your first boat or buying your fourth or fifth, this book should give food for thought. I hope it will also provide a yardstick by which any particular boat can be judged in all matters from seaworthiness to such details as the safety of the fuel system. At the back of the book I describe many different types of motor cruisers currently on the market and assess them critically. My aim is to look at the boats as if looking *in* through the shop window, rather than being inside trying to sell the goods. I have reported on many of the boats in *Practical Boat Owner*, while the preceding chapters are a compound of my training as a Naval Architect, experience and mistakes aboard boats I have owned and other people's ideas, notably those of Denny Desoutter, the Editor of PBO.

Introduction

The man who wishes to own a small family motor boat is not particularly well supplied with reading matter. Those books which *are* written about his pastime tend to be devoted to race boats or bigger craft.

This book is about motor boats in the 16–34 ft range, which can be used for cruising or fishing, weekending or day trips, on sea, river, lake or canal. I hope it will be used as a guide when choosing a boat, to assess possible hull performance, ease of handling, seaworthiness and comfort. These things are difficult to put in perspective in the excitement and pressures of buying one's dreamboat.

It is easy to fall in love with a particular boat and turn a blind eye to her defects. The heart must not entirely rule the head on such occasions, however, and it is important to have a firm idea of how well the craft is built and whether she will be suitable for the waters intended. On the other hand, the main purpose of any boat of this nature is to give pleasure, and for a man to buy a craft which may be technically ideal for the job, yet feel he is not particularly 'taken' with her lines, will eventually lead to dissatisfaction. There should be pride in the chosen boat, for her owner will be identified with her. Wives should also have their say in the choice if family cruising is intended.

1 Basic Choice

Motor cruisers are a mixed bunch—there are those which are fast and can plane, those which are slow but seaworthy and boats designed for particular waters. Furthermore, the accommodation varies widely. It is necessary early on to make up one's mind what type of motor cruiser to go for and the first part of this chapter sets out to help the reader formulate his requirements.

Key characteristics

Suitability
To cruise the narrow canals in England and Wales requires a beam of no more than 6 ft 10 in. To cruise along the coast requires a seaworthy and seakindly boat. Therefore only small boats of less than 18 or 19 ft can be satisfactorily designed for use on both narrow canals and the sea. A fast boat is like a fish out of water on canals and rivers where high speed is anti-social and usually illegal. A potentially fast boat powered with a small engine would also be unsatisfactory, mainly because handling at low speeds would probably be poor. To make use of a drying-out mooring, a boat must be able to take the ground without damaging herself or heeling over too far.

Speed
Because of hydrodynamic effects there is a hump in the power curve as boat speed increases, which can be used to roughly divide boats into slow displacement types and fast planing types. Because a particular boat has a hull shape which allows it to plane it does not mean that it is a 'better' boat than a displacement type; in order to achieve a high speed sacrifices in other aspects of the overall design must be made, notably in

seaworthiness and seakindliness and in handling at low speeds. It is exciting and exhilarating to race along at 25 knots but one gets used to it after a short time and in even slightly rough water a small boat will pound and slam on the waves. After an hour's determined slogging into a choppy sea the family may beg you to go home and sell the boat. Accelerations of 5 to 10 g can be experienced once or twice a second. Naturally some boats are much better than others but water is an unyielding element when hit hard. Apart from this the running costs of a fast boat are high. Fuel consumption may be ten times that of a displacement boat and the insurance premium may well be double.

Size

Obviously cost is a major factor here and also the number of berths required. Four berths can be squeezed into an 18-footer but the amount of space left over for 'living' will be very small. To live aboard in reasonable comfort for a few days at a time requires more than just a number of flat areas 6 ft 6 in × 2 ft covered with mattresses. As a general guide a 20-footer gives reasonable space for two people and a 24-footer for four.

The difference in roominess between a 20-footer and a 24-footer is quite amazing. The space gained for an extra few feet in length is considerable, because a longer boat usually also has more beam and more depth or headroom so the 'size' is increased in all three dimensions. Thus a 25-footer is roughly twice as roomy as a 20-footer. A 20-footer will have a beam of about 7 ft, while a 25-footer's will be about 8 ft 6 in which immediately means that the deck area (a multiple of length and breadth) will be increased by 50 per cent. An extra foot on the beam also has a big effect on the spaciousness and, as mooring charges are usually based on the overall length, extra beam gives a bigger craft without this extra expense.

The rapid increase in size with length reflects in the displacement and cost—hence the reason why a 25-footer is likely to be twice the cost of a 20-footer. The cost per ton of boat remains much the same. This rule applies in a much lesser degree to canal craft where beam and depth remain constant.

The displacement of a boat is a rather confusing term—it is

in fact exactly equal to the weight of the boat. Technically it means the weight of water which the boat displaces when floating and, by Archimedes' principle, this weight of water is exactly equal to the weight of the boat. Another term sometimes encountered is 'Thames Tonnage'. This has nothing to do with weight but is an arbitrary figure worked out from the length (L) and breadth (B)

$$\text{Thames Tonnage} = \frac{(L - B)B^2}{188}$$

Trailing
If the boat is to be regularly trailed to and from the water rather than kept on a mooring there is a definite limit to the size of boat which can be chosen, in terms of both length and weight. For one thing it depends on the size of the car which will be used. While it avoids the cost of a permanent mooring and cruising is not restricted to a particular area, the business of getting ready to go, trailing along crowded roads, finding a launching site and then actually launching can be quite a task. Launching sites are not numerous. If a trailable boat is the aim then it is wise to determine carefully the maximum size of boat you can cope with, bearing in mind the car, the parking space in the garden and the regulations.

Briefly the UK regulations (available from HMSO) are as follows. The maximum overall length of a trailer can be 7 metres (23 ft) excluding the draw bar although if the towing vehicle is of 2 tons weight or more it can tow trailers up to 12 metres (39 ft) long. The maximum width of a trailer can be 2·3 metres (7·54 ft) although the load may be 2·8 metres (9·18 ft) providing it does not extend more than 0·3 metres (0·98 ft) either side of the trailer.

A boat of about 1 ton is the most one should consider carrying on a two-wheeled trailer although the law allows 9 tons. A close coupled four-wheeled trailer gives better directional stability. Some European countries insist on four-wheeled trailers for even relatively light loads. Brakes are required for trailers of more than 102 kg (225 lb) unladen weight and providing the laden weight does not exceed 3560 kg

($3\frac{1}{2}$ tons) overrun brakes are permissible. Independent power operated brakes are necessary above the latter weight. In a number of States in the USA overrun brakes are banned.

The speed limit is basically 40 mph but if the laden weight of the trailer does not exceed the kerbside weight of the towing vehicle (in the case of trailers with brakes) or 60 per cent of the kerbside weight (in the case of trailers without brakes) one can tow at 50 mph. A circular '50' sign is required if the vehicle qualifies.

Trailer weight is not mentioned at all in the basic 40 mph regulations but obviously there is a practical limit to the combined weight of the trailer and boat in relation to the weight of the towing vehicle. The sensible limit is about 75 per cent of the weight of the car but it does depend on such things as the brakes and how many wheels the trailer has. The following guide is based on normal saloon cars and two-wheeled trailers fitted with overrun brakes.

850–1000 cc	8 cwt
1300 cc	15 cwt
1800 cc	20 cwt
2000 cc	25 cwt
Land-Rover	2 tons

If the trailer is fitted with four wheels and independent brakes the loads can be safely increased.

All trailers must have a suspension system, tyres must have a tread of at least one millimetre, mudguards are required and the regulations on lights must be complied with. These entail a board fitted with two red rear lamps, direction indicators, two red triangular reflectors, two red stop lights and a number plate lit at night.

The standard ball hitch nowadays is 50 mm rather than the old 2 inch. A winch is virtually a necessity with even the smallest cruiser. The lower leg and propeller of an outboard protruding from the stern of a trailed boat represents a hazard to other road users, especially if it is in the tilted position, and it is advisable to wrap the unit with foam padding and a canvas bag unless the outboard can be removed for trailing.

Inboard or outboard

This is another basic decision which affects the type of boat to choose and the pros and cons are discussed in Chapter 6. If the boat is to be trailed then an outboard which is light in weight has a distinct advantage. Generally speaking only motor cruisers under about 20 ft in length are outboard-powered, except inland craft where seaworthiness is not important and where even small outboards give enough power for boats up to about 30 ft in length.

The answers to the above questions will point to a particular type of motor boat. There is the small outboard-powered type with two berths in a small cabin, the larger type with living accommodation for about four people either displacement-hulled or capable of planing under the urge of powerful engines, and the cruiser designed mainly for fishing or day trips and having a large cockpit. Then there are out-and-out canal cruisers forming a distinct group of their own, and sports cruisers designed for performance and having less in the way of accommodation. This grouping is adopted in the concluding chapter where particular makes of cruisers are examined.

It is difficult to know what to call a boat powered solely by an engine. The terms motor cruiser, launch, power boat and motor yacht conjure up different pictures in different people's minds, but I think few people would argue with the following. A launch is a boat which has no cabin as such or perhaps just a small one in the bows and is ideal for day trips, fishing or taking the family along to a beach, or on a trip up a river; a launch may be fast or slow. The term power boat conjures up a fast motor boat crashing along in a welter of spray and is synonymous with race boat. Power cruiser suggests a similar sort of boat but 'cruiserfied' with the addition of better accommodation. Older terms include motor boat, cabin cruiser and motor yacht. One might expect a motor yacht to be a sailing yacht, modified and fitted with a large engine, but this sort of boat is more usually called a motor sailer. The term motor yacht is applied to large fully-powered craft—anything from 40 to 100 ft in length. Cabin cruiser has gone out of fashion, being replaced by motor cruiser which term implies a practical, sail-less craft fast or slow and with from one to eight berths for living on board and cruising from harbour to harbour or up a lazy river—in other words the powered counterpart of the family sailing yacht.

Buying or building

There are three ways in which your boat can be gained—by buying a new boat, by looking around for a second-hand boat or by building her yourself.

Buying a new boat is naturally the most costly way and is not at all the same as buying a new motor car. Unlike the car industry there are no giant-sized boat factories. Most builders produce only a few boats a week and many only ten to twenty craft a year, working in a simple shed and employing only a few men. For the customer this means he can watch his boat being built, stick his oar in over minor details and have extras fitted. This personal touch can be a great pleasure. With such yards there is likely to be pride in work and craftmanship. However, there is not the cost advantage which mass production offers and, despite the low overheads, the value for money is not as good as that of a motor car. There are showrooms where new boats can be bought there and then, but generally there is a waiting period. Payment is usually in stages as the craft is built. Marine mortgages are the order of the day but since repayment periods are short the monthly repayment sum is large.

Whether you will find the boat you are looking for on the second-hand market is largely a matter of patience and luck. The more expensive cruisers are usually put into the hands of brokers who advertise in the yachting press. Their commission is paid by the seller (8–10 per cent of the purchase price) and the buyer is treated with helpfulness and advice on surveys and financial matters. My own experience is that unless one bargains very hard the price paid is likely to be higher than if the sale is entirely private. In the first place the broker tends to put a high price on the boat and consequently one sees the same boat being advertised for month after month sometimes extending into years—the price in some cases gradually dropping. A professional survey is to be strongly recommended unless one is very knowledgeable about boat construction and engines and has the courage of one's convictions.

The third way of obtaining a boat is to build her yourself. Nowadays there is a wide range of GRP hulls available which takes care of the most difficult part of construction. The ideal arrangement is to set up the hull at home and then look upon the job as a long term project. A task like this is not to be underestimated. A bare hull is literally just that—a flimsy shell moulding lacking engine bearers, frames, gunwhale etc. A better proposition is to buy the hull, deck and superstructure all bonded together including hull stiffeners and engine bearers. The whole thing will then be raintight and the work of internal fitting-out and fitting the engine can start straight away. If the fitting of the engine presents a problem, there are several firms who supply the hull and superstructure externally complete together with the engine installed, so that all that is left is the time-consuming labour of internal fitting-out. There are plywood boat kits available and plans for building in ferro-cement which by all accounts is by far the cheapest way of building a hull. Building or fitting-out a boat is a huge task for one person to tackle in his spare time and it must not be taken on lightly. Many people have underestimated the amount of work and become discouraged half-way through. The amount of money to be saved by self-completion is not very great, but this is offset by the fact that the cost is spread out over a long period. It is the equipment which swells the cost, an anchor and chain, for example, costing the same whether bought separately from a chandler or included in the price of a new boat. This is an advantage of buying a second-hand boat—there is usually a great deal of equipment included.

The initial cost of a boat is one thing, the running cost another. Apart from mooring charges there will be charges for lifting-out and storage ashore, insurance premiums and fuel costs. To be financially correct one should also include depreciation in the total cost of running a boat. It is by no means of the same order as a car which after ten years is worth very little, as a ten year old boat is still, relatively, a youngster and may well change hands for around the same sum of money as her original selling price. The value of that money will of course have changed and by current standards be worth much less. This is the 'depreciation'. In any case the value of a boat is far more indeterminate than the value of a house or car and the asking price is usually considerably higher than the expected cash realisation. Then there is the cost of maintenance which if you do it yourself will not be much. Anti-fouling paint is about the biggest expense here. Some waterway authorities demand a licence fee. Marinas are expensive to use but convenient because, in most of them, one can step aboard and sail off at any state of the tide. There are cheaper swinging moorings or trot moorings between piles which may be in deep water or may dry out at low water.

Compromise in design

The design of a boat involves many compromises between conflicting requirements, and the best boats result from the best compromises. For instance, everybody would like full standing headroom in the cabin, but on boats of less than about 25 ft in length this means a tall cabin in relation to the length: the appearance of the boat suffers, the windage creates steering problems, and the top hamper reduces stability. A wide beam gives good initial stability and a roomy boat, but offers more resistance resulting in a loss of speed. A fast planing boat must have flat wide underwater sections aft and the weight of the boat must be kept to a minimum, so ballast is unacceptable; underwater appendages like keels cannot be tolerated and the resulting hull form is a far cry from the accepted seakindly fishing-boat hull. Speed is thus gained by the sacrifice of seaworthiness and comfort. Naturally designers strive to gain the advantages of a certain feature without unacceptable sacrifices. The deep vee hull form, or a modification of it, has enabled high speeds to be achieved with far less sacrifice in terms of comfort and seaworthiness than the older warped or shallow vee hard chine hulls. Not only do compromises have to be struck on the basic proportions and shape of a boat, but also on all sorts of details such as the siting of the engine and the fitting of the bunks and cupboards.

When GRP, or glass fibre as it was initially called, burst into the boat world in the 1950s the good sense and intuitive 'feel' for a well-designed boat was swept aside by the many firms who suddenly took to boat building. Here, they thought, was a wide open expanding market, using a material which anybody could master. The resulting boats gave GRP a bad name not only because of the poor quality of the moulding but because some boats were boxy, flat-bottomed, full-headroom things which earned the nicknames 'floating caravans' and 'plastic bath-tubs'. They were travesties of naval architecture and fortunately most of them have disappeared. The snag with GRP is that a plug and a mould have to be made. These are expensive items especially if there is a lot of curvature in the hull shape, and they are practically unalterable if modifications are seen to be desirable in the light of experience with the first boat on the water. In the days of wooden construction a process of trial and error gradually shaped boats over the centuries and the results are still applicable today. The sea does not change and there is much to be gained from adopting traditional shapes. The ubiquitous shallow vee hard chine hull is not one of those shapes. In the early days of GRP many small cruisers' hulls were never properly designed nor even drawn-up but just shaped by the eye of unqualified persons and, although this is far less common nowadays, there are still some hulls which make one wonder about their origin. A good hull, technically good and suitable for the job, is the prime requisite for a good cruiser. Nowadays the quality of construction is generally very good and one gets what one pays for. There are many excellently designed and built motor cruisers, particularly in the 22 to 28 ft range though the best designed are not necessarily the most expensive.

Safety at sea will be treated as an aspect of proper equipment and good seamanship, apart from having a seaworthy boat. Seamanship in this context is not so much knowing how to tie knots but knowing how to avoid or deal with potentially dangerous situations. It partly consists in such simple things as checking on the weather forecast before sailing, knowing how to deal with the engine if it stops and appreciating the effects of wind and tide in the locality in which you are to cruise.

A second source of propulsion is a great aid to safety. On a 16-footer this might be a small outboard or even a pair of oars. Twin engines are the ideal but an alternative not often seen nowadays is a 'father and son' arrangement, that is, a main engine on the centreline and a small engine on the wing.

Whatever the propulsion arrangement, an anchor and chain are absolutely essential items for any boat which puts to sea, whether in sheltered waters or offshore. There is a distinct difference in meaning between the terms 'inshore' and 'off-shore'. Generally inshore means within three miles of land and offshore, further out. Boat builders' claims for their 'offshore cruiser' should be examined sceptically.

I hope that, after reading this book, there will be no doubt in the mind of the newcomer to boating that 'driving' a motor cruiser is nowhere near the same as driving a motor car. Unfortunately there are few motor cruiser schools in existence, but it is worth mentioning the following:

East Berks Motor Cruiser School, 27, Rances Lane, Wokingham, Berks.
South Coast Motor Cruiser School, Beech House, Rowlands Castle, Hants.

2 Hull Shapes

The shape of the hull of the motor cruiser you choose will determine her speed potential, stability, how well she rides in rough water and, to some extent, the spaciousness of the accommodation.

A boat chosen for crossing the Channel to France at 25 knots will have a very different hull form from a traditional canal boat, cruising the canals at 3 knots. Even if one put an enormous horsepower in a traditional canal boat it would never go very fast. We shall see that all boats may be classed as fast or slow, and that if a boat is slow no amount of power will change its character to that of a fast type. Then again hull forms are divided into round bilge and hard chine, the latter being invariably described nowadays as 'deep vee', whether or not the hull form really warrants the label.

Hull design is a complicated science and has led to extended research programmes aimed at improving the speeds of ships. The results have little relevance to boats, so boat designers are rather hamstrung. But general principles still hold true and it is these that this chapter tries to explain. We are looking at the problem not from the designer's point of view, but from a shop-window point of view—seeing what hull shapes are suitable for what speeds, and learning the merits and vices of the multitude of underwater shapes seen on boats currently on the market.

Resistance to motion

Let us start with a sedate speed of 4 or 5 knots and examine what constitutes a suitable hull shape for this speed. Consider a motor boat travelling along in calm water at a steady engine speed. The engine burns fuel, producing power, and the propeller converts about half that power into thrust-power which, when the boat is going along at a steady speed, will exactly equal the resistance of the hull to forward motion. The net thrust from the propeller will exactly equal the force needed to push the boat along (the 'resistance' of the hull). If the hull shape were different and had less resistance, the same engine would push the boat along faster.

The resistance to motion of the hull is caused in several ways. First there is the friction of the water rubbing along the bottom of the hull. The rougher the surface and the faster the boat the more the resistance. Secondly there is the wave pattern the boat creates in its wake. These waves are the visible evidence of energy being created and wasted by the hull which in turn has to be supplied by the engine and its fuel. The best hull therefore has a smooth surface and a shape that creates little wash. Other sources of resistance come from the separation of water flow causing turbulence due to a lack of streamlining, for instance a deeply immersed transom at slow speeds. There is also air resistance and the drag of rudders, outdrive or outboard legs, keels etc.

The magnitude of each type of resistance varies at different boat speeds. At very slow speeds the majority of the total resistance comes from friction; at faster speeds wave making is predominant and at planing speeds friction is again important but so also is the drag from appendages.

Hump speed
Some of the waves created by a boat have a drastic influence on possible increases of speed beyond what will be referred to as the 'hump'. The hump is a natural barrier which results from these waves and for a boat 20–25 ft long represents 7–8 knots. This phenomenon occurs at the same speed whatever the hull shape. One can reduce the great increase of resistance at the hump by changes in hull shape, but the speed at which the hump occurs is solely due to the natural laws that govern the behaviour of waves in water. There is a relation between the speed of a water wave and its length from crest to crest.

Wave length (crest to crest) ft	Speed knots
2·2	2
8·9	4
20	6
35	8
56	10

With this in mind consider again our motor boat travelling along at a steady speed, still in calm water. The bow throws off waves which angle out obliquely on each side, and the stern may do the same. These waves are not important—they leave the hull and have no further influence. But along the hull and astern of it are transverse waves (Figure 1) which trail along

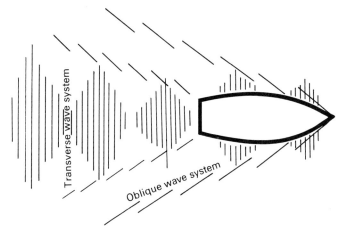

1   The wave system set up by a boat travelling at displacement speeds

in the same direction as the boat. These are long, low waves, not so impressive as the oblique foam and wash waves coming from the bows, but it is these which really cause the 'dragginess' of the hull. These waves show clearly on the profile of a boat moving at increasing speeds up to the hump speed (Figure 2).

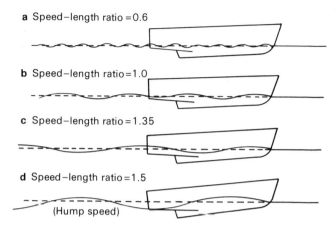

2 *The transverse wave system set up by a boat travelling at different speeds*

It is primarily the entrance of the hull, the forebody, which produces pressure fluctuations in the surrounding water making a wave crest at the bow. Now if the forebody is pushing along at 6 knots the length of the wave produced will be 20 ft from crest to crest. If the boat is 20 ft long the stern will be on a crest as in Figure 2c. If the boat is 10 ft long the stern will be in the trough of the wave as in Figure 2d. In this last case the boat will be trying to climb its own wave and the stern will tuck down and the bows lift—it will be at the hump speed. In the case of a 40 ft boat there will be several small crests along the length of the hull at 6 knots, and there will be little fuss or wash. The longer the boat the higher the speed can be before the stern is settled in the trough of the pressure wave created by the bows. This is fundamental for any hull shape and is the limit for all so-called displacement boats, i.e. heavy boats or those not having very powerful engines.

Speed:length ratio

This natural interplay between hull and water forms a very simple and effective rule-of-thumb for assessing the speed potential of a boat, particularly displacement boats. We have seen that the speed of a boat determines the length of the wave of its own creation on which it must sit and thus, knowing the length of a boat, its attitude at various speeds is known—whether it is fussily trying to climb up its own bow wave or gently cruising along with several crests along its length. A figure can be put to this attitude and it is called the speed:length ratio.

$$\text{speed:length ratio} = \frac{\text{speed (knots)}}{\text{square root of length on waterline (feet)}}$$

For example, take a boat 16 ft long on the waterline. The square root of this is 4, so that a speed of 4 knots represents a speed:length ratio of 1. Eight knots would give a speed:length ratio of 2. Taking the square root of the length overcomes the fact that the length of a wave goes up as the square of the speed. The length dimension which matters is, of course, the length on the waterline. We can now put values to the profiles in Figure 2. The hump speed (Figure 2d) gives a ratio of around 1·5–1·7, while economical speeds give ratios below 1·35.

Table 1. Reference table for speed:length ratios.
Speed:length ratio = speed (knots) divided by the square root of the waterline length (ft)

Length on waterline ft	Speed:length ratio					
	0·6	1·0	1·35	1·5	2·5	5·0
16	2·4 knots	4·0	5·4	6·0	10·0	20·0
18	2·55	4·25	5·7	6·4	10·6	21·2
20	2·7	4·5	6·0	6·7	11·2	22·4
22	2·8	4·7	6·3	7·0	11·7	23·4
24	3·0	4·9	6·7	7·4	12·3	24·6
26	3·1	5·1	6·9	7·7	12·8	25·6
28	3·2	5·3	7·1	7·9	13·2	26·4
30	3·3	5·5	7·4	8·2	13·7	27·5
32	3·4	5·7	7·6	8·5	14·1	28·2
	Very slow gentle cruise e.g. canal boats	Economical cruise with little fuss or effort— very little wash	Beginning of 'hump'. Wash becoming obtrusive. Economical up to these speeds	The 'hump'. Stern in the trough	Threshold of planing.	Planing well. Greater speeds can be considered 'very fast'

The beauty of this ratio is that it applies to any length of boat. It also has a real hydrodynamic significance but this is unnecessary knowledge for choosing a motor cruiser.

What is important is to appreciate the effect of the boat's own wave system on the speed potential of the hull. The resistance of any hull increases very rapidly as the speed : length ratio approaches the hump. In other words, an increase in engine power has little effect on the speed achieved. A typical resistance curve (Figure 3) for speeds up to the hump (speed : length ratio = 1·5–1·7) shows the small resistance and

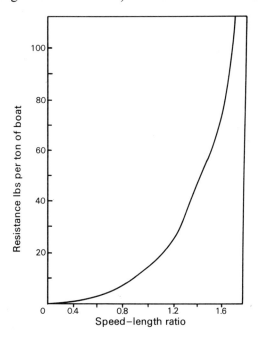

3   Typical curve of resistance up to the hump speed

hence engine power required to achieve a speed : length ratio of less than 0·9 and the massive resistance of a hull being driven at speed : length ratios over about 1·35. The general shape of this curve is much the same for any hull shape, whether a planing boat or a barge, but of course the bluffer the boat the greater the actual resistances become, although differences only begin to show above a speed : length ratio of about 1·2.

But the general trend remains the same—economical, quiet progress at speed:length ratios of up to about 1·2 and uneconomical speeds approaching the hump. The wash at speeds approaching the hump will be increasingly heavy and the boat will squat by the stern.

Thus the choice of hull shape is relatively unimportant if the boat is only intended to travel at speeds up to a speed: length ratio of about 1·2. The difference in engine power necessary between a box-shaped boat and a round-bilged, sweet-lined boat will be small and, in any case, the actual powers involved will be small—around 10 h.p. per ton. The choice of hull shape becomes increasingly important as the intended speed:length ratio rises beyond 1·2.

Another important use of this speed:length ratio is that for any displacement boat one can take the waterline length and estimate fairly accurately its economical cruising speed and its maximum speed. A 27-footer (generally boat lengths are given overall) will have a waterline length of perhaps 25 feet. The square root of this figure is 5, so the speed:length ratio at 5 knots will be 1·0.

A good cruising speed will be 1·1 to 1·2 × 5 knots, i.e. 5·5 to 6 knots. If the boat is a displacement type the maximum speed even with a large engine of, say, 60–70 h.p. will be little more than 1·5 × 5 knots, i.e. 7·5 knots. If an 80 or 100 h.p. engine is fitted the speed might increase by another knot, depending on the shape of the hull and all-up weight of the boat.

As the hull shape, from a hydrodynamic point of view, is not of great importance in the case of a displacement cruiser, other features can be worked in to give good seaworthiness, stability and more space in the cabin, without much sacrifice in speed. The hull can be deep with a good keel, the boat can be heavy (both features giving good seaworthiness), ballast and a broad beam can be incorporated for stability and the cabin floor lowered to give better headroom. The sacrifice in speed, or the increase in engine power to give the same speed, is relatively insignificant. Notwithstanding these statements a rounded, smooth-lined hull is still superior to a shoe-box, if too much speed or power is not to be sacrificed. Features which needlessly add resistance should always be avoided. For instance, badly faired bilge keels and a square cut end to the centre keel are points on which to check. Bilge keels are often just thick planks of wood with the edges rounded off. The ends, especially the after end, should taper off to a point. Also, if bilge keels are positioned out of line with the flow of water over the bottom they can cause a great deal of drag. Unfortunately, this is something upon which it is very difficult to check. The keel ending immediately in front of the propeller

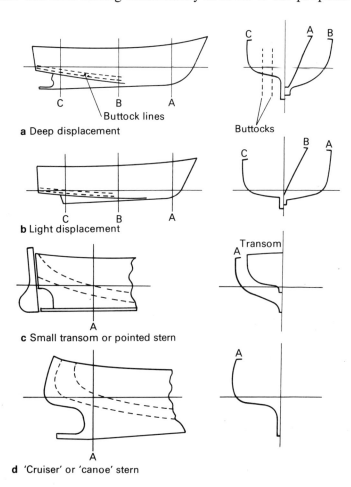

a Deep displacement

Buttock lines

Buttocks

b Light displacement

Transom

c Small transom or pointed stern

d 'Cruiser' or 'canoe' stern

4   Displacement hull shapes

should also taper off. Apart from the drag created, turbulence is shed into the propeller causing vibration and perhaps cavitation. The rudder when situated immediately behind the propeller has a very fast flow of water over it, and a smooth shape with a rounded leading edge and tapered trailing edge minimises unavoidable drag. Sometimes one sees rudders which are thick, square-ended and even stiffened with vertical strips on each side. Water does not like to be forced around protrusions and along unfair lines, so look at all the underwater appendages to see if they are faired-in and will allow a smooth flow of water.

Displacement shapes can have transom, cruiser or pointed sterns—up to speed:length ratios of about 1·3 it does not matter—but whereas a transom-sterned boat may be forced beyond 1·5, a pointed or cruiser stern is most definitely limited to a maximum of 1·5. Such sterns have buttock lines which rise rapidly as they approach the stern, which kills any chance of further speed. (Buttock lines show the shape of the bottom of the after portion of the hull, at various distances off the centre line, looking sideways at the hull.)

To conclude this first section on low-speed displacement hull shapes the sketches in Figure 4 show some common forms. The important points to look for in such hulls are the depth of the hull proper below the waterline, the depth and extent of the keel, the shape of sections forward, aft and amidships and the sweep of the buttock lines.

Over the hump

The hull shape becomes increasingly important as the design speed of the boat increases up to and beyond the hump. To achieve high speeds some sacrifice must be made of other qualities. In the previous paragraphs we saw that the weight of the boat and the buttock lines are increasingly important if speeds up to and beyond the hump are required. It is easy to understand why weight becomes important—any method of transport has this problem—but more difficult to understand is how the hull shape can be modified to allow more speed.

The bows-up attitude of the boat at the hump must be reduced and the whole length of the hull considered as the entrance or forebody. The bows need to be made slim and fine. The aft end of the boat requires to be lifted and the bottom of the boat made flat, looking at it in profile, rather than curved. Lift is achieved at the stern by making the transom wide at the waterline and the bottom, flat aft, i.e. the buttock lines must run flat and nearly horizontal. A transom stern is now vital. Thus when the boat is approaching the hump and sinks by the stern, the flat bottom aft presents itself in a wedging action which creates lift. Excessive trim is avoided and more engine power will produce more speed. As the boat accelerates over the hump, the second crest of the wave produced by the hull will move further and further astern. The whole hull is now the entrance—it is now supported on its own bow wave. This modified displacement shape (Figure 5) is ideal for speed : length ratios of between 1·5 and 2·5 and is usually called 'fast-displacement' or 'fast-round-bottom'.

A form of this type must have fine underwater bow lines. The angle of the bows at the waterline must be sharp and the maximum breadth at the waterline only obtained aft of amidships. To compensate for the lack of buoyancy forward, the bows should flare sharply outwards above the water to reduce plunging in a head sea. The flare should continue right aft and a spray chine or knuckle is a good thing, both items reducing the chance of water climbing up the sides and increasing resistance, besides making the boat wet.

The other hull shape which can be used to exceed the hump is the hard chine form. The bottom meets the sides in a hard corner, hence the term. Basically the buttock lines are again flat and the transom wide with the 'wedging' action taken further still. Once over the hump the lift forces become significant and eventually lift the boat bodily, causing the hull to plane over, rather than through, the water. Wave making is much reduced. In fact most of the weight of the boat is supported by these lift forces rather than buoyancy forces. Planing can only take place at a speed : length ratio of over 2·5, although some types of hull start to plane later. Once planing is achieved the way is open to faster and faster travel. The

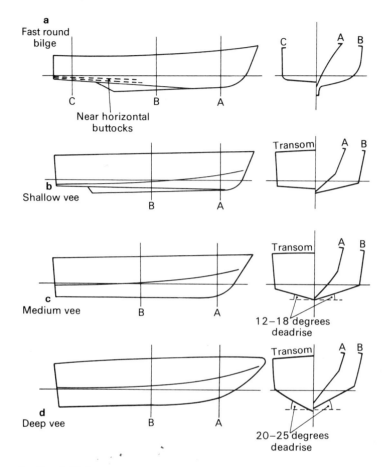

a
Fast round bilge

Near horizontal buttocks

C   A B

b
Shallow vee

Transom   A B

c
Medium vee

Transom   A B

12–18 degrees deadrise

d
Deep vee

Transom   A B

20–25 degrees deadrise

5   Fast hull shapes

increase of resistance as speed increases is then quite reasonable, unlike the rate of increase up to the hump (see Figure 12 on p. 42). Thus one can profitably fit a bigger engine and expect more speed. A hard chine hull can also be usefully employed at the not-quite-planing speed:length ratios of 1·5 to 2·5 in competition with the fast-round-bilge type. From the point of view of resistance and power there is not a lot to choose, but for seakindliness the round-bilge variety scores.

Shallow vee to deep vee

Before the deep vee came into fashion most hard-chine craft were similar to the sketch in Figure 5b. The veed forward sections gradually flatten until the bottom of the boat aft is practically flat. The two sides of the bottom are twisted or warped hence the expression 'warped hard-chine'. This form planes readily, starting at a speed:length ratio of about 2·5, and uses the engine's power efficiently up to a speed:length ratio of about 5 (25 knots on a 25-footer). It slams badly in rough water and steers badly at slow speeds unless a deep keel is fitted which will, of course, create drag at high speed. It is a good form for lakes or other sheltered waters where there are no speed limits, but for sea work the shape has its limitations.

The tendency to pound created a poor name for hard-chine craft, and it was partly this that caused the moderate vee and then the deep vee hull form to be developed. The first development made the forward sections deeper and more veed, thus bringing the chine line higher at the bow and then, later, made the vee of the bottom constant from amidships to aft (Figure 5c).

This is sometimes called the monohedron form. The angle of the bottom of the after body to the horizontal (the deadrise) is usually 10°–15°. This form takes more power to plane and it generally offers more resistance up to speed:length ratios of around 5. The hump is more prolonged and the onset of planing less distinct. With a shallow vee hull the onset of planing is very noticeable, the boat flattening off and accelerating away dramatically. The deeper the vee of the bottom the less efficient it is as a planing surface, and the greater the struggle to get on to the plane. A flat plate will skim over the water extremely efficiently, whereas if it is bent in the middle longitudinally it will have to carve a vee in the water, and naturally the drag is higher. This is the case for speed:length ratios of up to about 5.

The true deep vee variety has a deadrise of 20°–25° from amidships to the transom and a long drawn-out bow with the sections becoming only a little steeper towards the bow (Figure 5d). At present this form is the best for really high speed work (speed:length ratios of over 5) and rough water.

In fact, the extreme vee of the planing surfaces does not detract from the efficiency of planing at very high speeds, because the chief source of resistance is changed. We have seen that wave-making resistance is predominant for speed:length ratios up to about 2·5. Above this, so long as planing is achieved, surface friction (the drag of the water on the underwater surfaces) predominates. There is also a small drag induced by the creation of lift—like an aeroplane wing—the inevitable result of the wing or planing surface being set at a small angle of attack. There is too the not inconsiderable drag from the propeller shaft and rudder. A shallow or moderate vee hull at very high speeds tends to flatten out her running trim, thus again immersing the forward sections. This causes a great deal of extra surface drag with little compensating lift. A deep vee hull rides at a greater angle of trim at all speeds and the surface area in contact with the water is less. So, although a deep vee hull needs a great deal of power to struggle onto the plane, and more power than a moderate vee at speed:length ratios of up to 5, above this it tends to be less resistant. It also scores in terms of motion in rough water.

In practice most motor cruisers are either shallow vee or moderate vee, despite the claims of some manufacturers. A true deep vee hull has some characteristics which are not really suitable for family cruisers—the 'tippiness' at rest and the inability to take a drying-out mooring, for example. The long drawn-out bow does not make the most of the overall length—there is much wasted space inside. The race-boat style of deep vee can be modified to give a more sensible family cruiser but, nevertheless the medium vee (10° to 15° deadrise) is far more suitable. It is also more economical in engine power at the speed:length ratios that most people prefer or can afford; i.e. speed:length ratios of up to 5 (22 knots on a 20 foot waterline length).

There are many small variations of the three basic hard-chine forms. For instance, to increase the stability at rest of a deep vee hull, the bottom near the chine can be flattened out so that the chines are in the water when the boat is stationary (Figure 6). At speed the chines run clear of the water so that the portion of the hull actually immersed has a large deadrise.

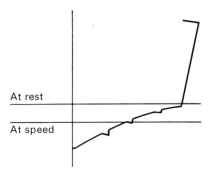

6   Modification of the deep vee to give better stability at rest

Nevertheless in rough water the flatter portions near the chines may pound.

One or two small cruisers have a triple hull configuration of similar shape to the familiar Boston whaler and Dell Quay Dory open boats. The hull form shown in Figure 7 is sometimes called 'gull-wing' or 'cathedral'. It planes readily mainly because the bottom aft is very flat, and also gives much more room inside the cabin, because the breadth of the hull is

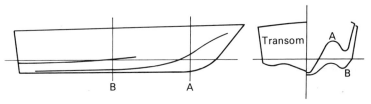

7   Cathedral, gull wing or triple hull shape

maintained for almost the whole length of the boat. The bows are square rather than pointed. The ride is not so good as that of a hull with veed bows, but is acceptable for speed:length ratios of up to 5.

The whole range of speeds and hull shapes has now been described. The graph (Figure 12, on p. 42) gives an overall view of the various hull forms and their potential speed. The hump can be seen which divides boats roughly into fast and slow types, while the fast-round-bilge type bridges the gap. Fundamentally, for a displacement boat one can say that 'speed equals length'—the longer the boat the faster it will go—while for a planing boat 'speed equals power' i.e. the aim is to install high power in a light hull.

Suitability

If the choice is a displacement cruiser, speeds of up to $6\frac{1}{2}$ knots on an 18 ft waterline, and $7\frac{1}{2}$ knots on a 25 ft waterline can be expected, while weight saving and sleekness of hull form need assume little importance. Other qualities such as seaworthiness and comfort can be obtained. Fitting a large engine to such a boat is wasteful of fuel and any extra speed obtained is minimal. The real displacement hull shape approaches that of a keel sailing boat, with deep sections and perhaps permanent ballast incorporated. In practice there are few motor cruisers currently on the market which are true displacement types. On the other hand, there are many round-bilge non-planing cruisers which are called displacement types. With shallow hulls and relatively low weight for their length they have neither the kindly motion, damped by great weight, of the true displacement hull or sufficiently flat buttocks to ride over the hump and qualify as a fast round-bilge type; these types will be referred to as 'mock displacement'. Nevertheless, a hull of this type is preferable to a hard-chine boat, particularly a shallow hard-chine, if speeds are intended to be only up to 6 or 7 knots. From a resistance point of view there is nothing much to choose, but a mock displacement hull will pound less in rough water and will handle better.

Although the obvious choice of hull form for displacement speeds is round-bilge, it is very common for a hard-chine boat to be powered intentionally for displacement speeds. A large number of canal and river cruisers are shallow vee hard-chine. As explained in Chapter 10 the use of such a hull form often creates difficulties in steering, especially in a strong wind. Also the oblique waves formed at the bow are larger than those from a corresponding round-bilge form. Wash is a particular nuisance on river and canals, not only because of the eroding effect on the banks, but also because of the effect on other boats moored to the bank. On the other hand the hard-chine form is more stable and gives more space inside the hull. And then, of course, from the manufacturers' point of view it is easier and cheaper to make a plug and hence a mould for a hard-chine hull than a round-bilge one.

The natural development over the centuries of traditional local craft has led to distinctive types of boat and hull shape. The Yorkshire coble, Scottish fishing boats and Dutch botters and boeiers are well known examples, but there are dozens of such craft, with fascinating names such as baldie, bawley, fifee, Galway hooker, tosher, and quay punt, all distinct types of working boat which used to be a common sight in particular areas around the British Isles. These were originally powered by sail, but several have continued to be built and powered by engines. A few motor cruisers today owe their hull shapes to these old traditional designs. With minor modifications, yet keeping the overall looks, a happy combination of tradition and modern materials can be made. Certainly there is nothing wrong with using the results of centuries of unconscious development. All these old designs were, of course, displacement craft, bred to cope with rough water and, despite all the efforts of modern research, substantially better hull shapes for slow speed seawork have not yet been invented.

There are one or two small cruisers today based on fishing boat hulls or work boats, and then there are so-called traditional canal boats and river craft with slipper sterns. The narrow canals in England and Wales can only admit craft of 6 ft 10 in beam because of the width of the locks. When cargo-carrying barges were used on the canals, to give the maximum carrying capacity the hulls were naturally made boxlike, rectangular sectioned with flat bottoms. The resistance characteristics are poor, but then only horse-drawn speeds were contemplated. Nowadays the motor cruisers based on the old canal barges have a natural grace and practicability, while speeds have not increased. This cannot happen anyway because of the shallow water and need to conserve the canal banks. Canal speeds on British waterways are 3 to 4 knots which, on a length of 40 ft, for instance, represents a speed-length ratio of 0·5 to 0·6; i.e. not only below the hump but

below the sea-going economical speed:length ratio of 1·0 to
1·2. The resistance is trifling (see Figure 3), the wave-making
hardly noticeable. In fact, most of the resistance comes from
water friction. The engine power required is small. Thus, a
13 h.p. engine is adequate for a 40 ft traditional canal boat
weighing perhaps 10 tons. Even a 20 ft boat only operates at
a speed:length ratio of 0·7 to 0·9 at speeds of 3–4 knots.

The hull feature which distinguishes the British traditional
canal cruiser from the resin-glass shallow vee counterpart is
the depth of the hull. The former usually has an absolutely
flat bottom about 18–21 in below the surface of the water.
The shallow vee hull has only a few inches immersion and
consequently the boat lies on rather than in the water. From a
hydrodynamic point of view there is little to be gained from
having a shallow hull if speeds are to be only 3–4 knots. In
other words, a light 25 ft resin-glass canal cruiser will be
insignificantly faster than a heavy steel traditional cruiser of
the same length when powered by the same small engine
horsepower.

Many light resin-glass cruisers are intended only for the
canals, and perhaps rivers, and really there is little excuse for
making the boats so light and shallow-drafted. It is more
difficult to gain headroom in the cabin and the boat skitters
about in a strong wind, but it must be conceded that with a
total draft of perhaps only 12 in, practically all available
canals can be cruised. Many shallow vee hulled motor cruisers
are marketed as suitable for canal, estuary *and* offshore. For
sea-going work the manufacturers recommend larger engines
and make the boats strong enough to plane. When the beam is
restricted to 6 ft 10 in the length of these multi-purpose boats
may not much exceed 20 ft, otherwise the stability at sea would
suffer from lack of beam. Even so, the design of such a boat
falls between two stools. Neither on the canal nor at sea are
they ideal.

Where the maximum beam is not restricted it pays to increase
it as much as possible. From a purely hydrodynamic point of
view the narrower the hull the less the resistance, both for
displacement and planing boats, but other considerations
override this fact. Nowadays the beam is set at the greatest

that the length can take. This is sensible, despite the slight loss of performance. It means more boat for the overall length (length costs money, both in first cost and mooring costs), and also greater stability.

To recap on the suitability of planing hull shapes, probably the best form for estuary and coastal work is the medium vee; i.e. with a deadrise of 10° to 15° from amidships to the transom. On small cruisers of say, less than 20 ft, to adopt this amount of deadrise makes the boat very 'tippy' when at rest and a shallower vee is better. The smaller the boat the greater the compromise that has to be made and the greater the limitations of the boat. The deep vee certainly cannot be applied to these small boats without sacrificing important qualities. Above 20 ft a modified deep vee is acceptable. The race boat style can be foreshortened and the bottom near the chine turned down to give stability at rest.

Practical points

Can she take the ground? This is a most important point to consider, especially if the boat's permanent mooring dries out. Not only must the boat sit reasonably upright so that the returning tide does not flood over the gunwales, but the propellers and rudders must be protected from taking the weight of the boat. Hard ground such as sand or shingle is much worse than soft mud from this point of view. Displacement boats fitted with an inboard engine are usually quite capable of taking the ground (Figure 8a). Bilge keels will keep the hull more upright on hard ground. With an outboard or outdrive powered craft there is again usually no problem, because in both cases the propeller can be swung up above the keel line. The inboard-powered planing craft is the most difficult on which to provide protection for the stern gear, because of the absence of a keel and the flat buttock lines. A keel deep enough to give protection would lose the boat several knots of top speed and cause dangerous instability in sharp turns at high speed. This is the case with medium or deep vee hulls, particularly with a single propeller on the centre line.

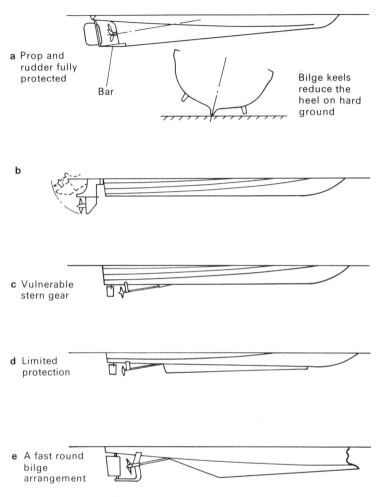

a Prop and
rudder fully
protected

Bar

Bilge keels
reduce the
heel on hard
ground

b

c Vulnerable
stern gear

d Limited
protection

e A fast round
bilge
arrangement

8   Taking the ground

With shallow vee hulls it is sometimes possible to arrange a
short but deep enough keel (Figure 8d) and such a boat can
usually take a mud mooring without harm.

The rake of the stem is important for anchor work (Figure
9). The anchor will foul a straight vertical stem more easily
than one that is well raked. On the other hand a sharply raked
bow will lose waterline length and potential speed in the case
of a displacement boat. Also one usually pays for a mooring

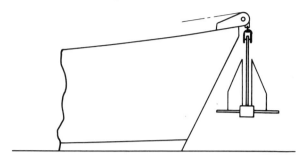

9 A raked bow makes anchor work easier

per foot of overall length, another incentive to choose an upright stem. A sharply raked transom merely reduces the waterline length to no advantage. A transom stern as opposed to a pointed or rounded stern gives more space inside the hull for a given overall length, and makes an easier place to climb onto the boat from a dinghy, particularly if the water is choppy. On the other hand, the sharp corners of the transom usually take knocks when leaving a jetty or lock. Tumblehome (Figure 10) lowers the point of contact between a jetty or lock

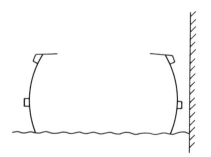

10 If the sides are tumblehomed scrapes are likely low down

and the hull so that an additional rubbing strake needs to be fitted. There is little virtue in tumblehome (which is a relic of sailing ship days) and one wonders why some boats are still made with this feature.

More on planing hulls

Spray strakes are in evidence on most planing boats nowadays, their job being, as their name implies, to cut down the amount of spray produced. They are most important at the fore end of the hull and in deeply veed boats (Figure 11). There is some

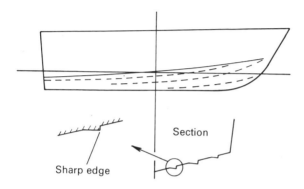

Section

Sharp edge

11   Spray strakes for a medium vee hull. They should continue right aft on a deep vee hull

argument as to how much lift they do produce, but it has been established by tank tests that they have very little effect on resistance and hence speed, except on deep-vee hulls. On moderate vee hulls they are most usefully placed forward on the bottom to cut down spray and prevent water climbing up the steeply veed forward section and increasing the wetted area. This would increase the frictional resistance enormously as well as making the boat wet. There is no need for the in-board strakes to run right aft as there they would be in solid water and would do nothing except create turbulence and drag. The strake adjacent to the chine can usefully be run right aft, because at high speed it will keep the chine drier further aft than would otherwise be the case. On a shallow vee hull the chine is often low enough and distinct enough to do all the water deflecting necessary, but there is no harm in spray strakes along the bottom right forward.

On a deep vee hull it is a different matter altogether—indeed the hull might not work at all if not so fitted. The strakes should run all the way along the bottom. At high speed a deep vee rides on a triangular area of bottom right aft and the water flow is slightly diagonal. Spray strakes are thus necessary in this area to prevent or at least aerate the water climbing up the vee of the bottom.

It was mentioned earlier that the appendages on a fast boat created a significant proportion of the total drag. Apart from spray strakes which can have a very slightly beneficial effect, keels, bilge keels, propeller shafts, shaft brackets, outdrive or outboard legs and rudders are all appendages which create unwanted drag. This is why the bottoms of fast boats appear naked. Thus keels, if any, are made small, bilge keels are rarely fitted and rudders are made as small as possible. The surface area and the resulting friction of these items is mainly responsible for their drag. Shaft brackets and outboard or outdrive legs are made as streamlined as possible with a small frontal area. The lack of keel and the smallness of the rudder can cause difficulties steering at low speed.

An important characteristic of a planing boat is the angle of trim at which she runs. Although one cannot predict whether a certain boat will run at a good trim or not, the subject is worth mentioning here while on the general subject of fast boats. When properly planing, a shallow vee hull should run at about 4° trim, i.e. the bows should lift until the boat is angled at 4°. A trim of less than this will seriously increase the resistance. This is because as the bows drop down into the water the wetted area becomes much greater. Similarly too much trim will be detrimental, although not nearly to the same degree. The greater the deadrise the greater should be the planing angle—6° with a deep vee hull. These figures only apply when the boat is properly planing; i.e. at speed:length ratios of over, say, 3·5. At hump speeds and up to a speed:length ratio of 2·5 the trim will naturally be greater than these figures because the boat is trying hard to gain lift.

Correction of trim can be done by wedges, trim tabs, ballast tanks, altering the angle of the outboard or outdrive leg, or merely by shifting weight forward or aft. A wedge on the underside of the transom is not often used, trim tabs are usually an extra and ballast tanks in the bows are rare. Trim tabs and ballast tanks enable the trim to be changed at will which is an advantage, because a lesser trim gives a better ride in rough water. Trim tabs only work well at planing speeds—their effect is dependent on the speed of the water flowing over them. With an outdrive or outboard there is usually an adjustment for tilting the leg so that the propeller is thrusting slightly upwards to lift the stern or downwards to lift the bows. Some makes of outdrive and outboard can be fitted with a device to trim the leg while under way, which is a very elegant solution.

Weight is important to any fast boat. One cannot load a small boat with extras and heavy equipment and expect the performance to be unaltered. This particularly applies to boats powered for speed: length ratios between 2·5 and 4. If planing is marginal anyway, an extra passenger may prevent planing and halve the top speed.

The bottom of a planing boat needs to be kept clean to stop the increase in frictional resistance which fouling produces, but there is no need actually to polish the bottom—a normal paint surface is 99 per cent as friction-free as one glass-smooth.

From these comments it will be appreciated that to give its best performance, a fast boat needs to be tuned and then well maintained, rather like a racing yacht or a sports car.

Tank testing

If a boat is claimed to have been tank tested this is a sign that the hull shape is probably good and that the claimed speed is realistic. Not many hulls are in fact tank tested because it is a costly business. Many hull shapes are designed by eye by the builder, which may or may not bring forth a good hull, but an increasing number of boats on the market are independently designed. In this case a production run is usually envisaged so the cost of tank testing can be borne. Ideally, several models are built with varying lines, tank tested, and the one with the least resistance chosen, but in practice this is usually too expensive and only the projected hull form is tested. This is not a waste of time because the tank people would be able to tell the builder before testing whether the hull form was any good for the projected speed. Also the test will confirm or refute the estimated speed with different engine powers. Simple tank testing involves dragging a model up and

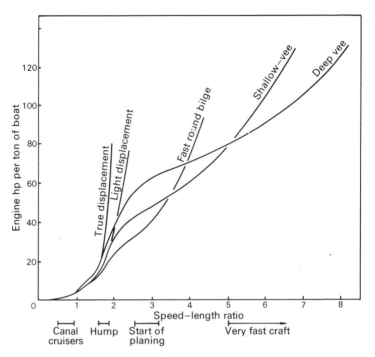

12 *A broad pictorial view covering the whole speed spectrum.*
Note the low horsepowers required for canal work and the very high
horsepowers required to get over the hump. Deep vees are best at
really high speeds while the fast round-bilge hull becomes
uneconomical early on. The graph also brings out the importance of
the power: weight ratio for planing craft and the relative
unimportance of weight for displacement craft. To plane at all
requires 60 to 80 h.p. per ton

down a tank of calm water and measuring its resistance, from which the required engine power can be worked out. Tests in rough water are even more expensive and not as yet common practice in the boat world.

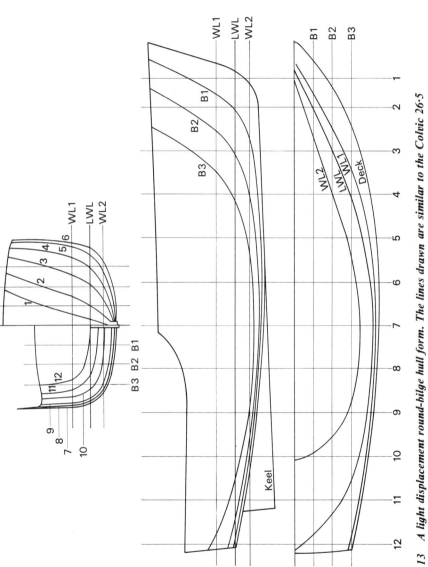

13 *A light displacement round-bilge hull form. The lines drawn are similar to the Colvic 26·5*

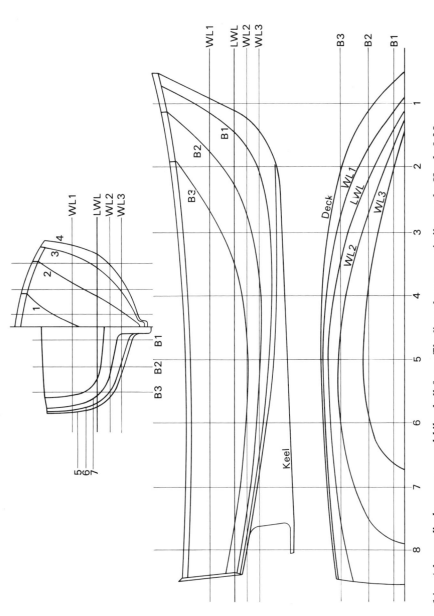

14   *A heavy displacement round-bilge hull form. The lines drawn are similar to the Hardy 8·25*

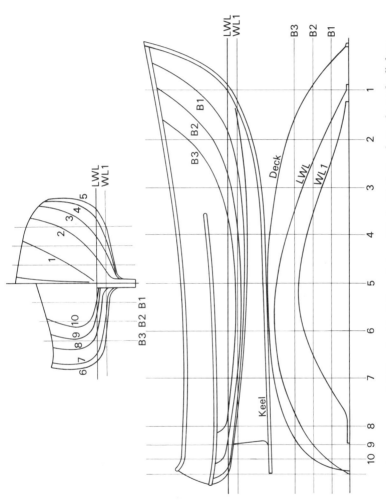

15   *A canoe-sterned fishing boat hull form but modified with flatter buttocks and a lighter displacement. The lines are similar to the Island Plastics 23*

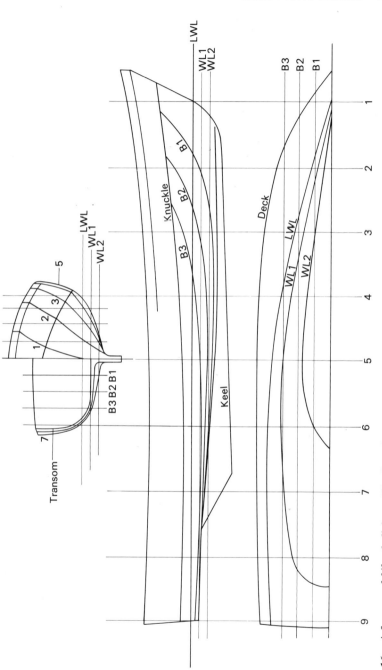

16 *A fast round-bilge hull form. The lines drawn are similar to the Keith Nelson 34*

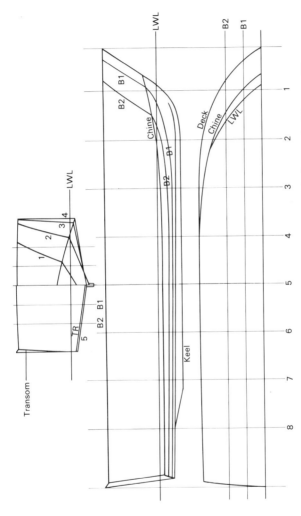

17   *A shallow vee hard-chine hull form. The lines drawn are similar to the Norman 23*

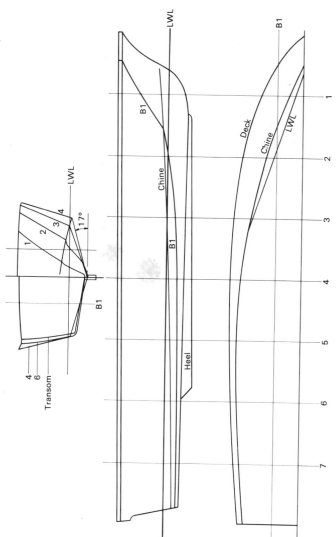

18 A warped shallow to medium vee hard-chine hull form. The lines are similar to the Senior 31

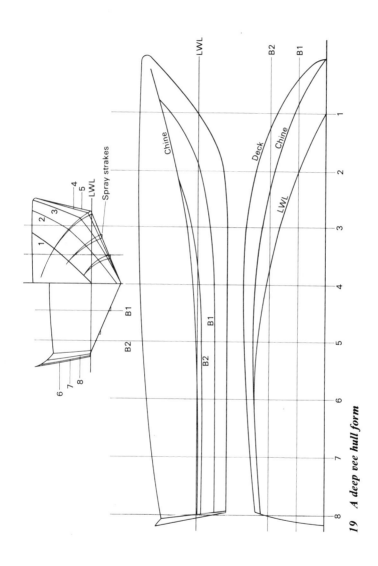

19 A deep vee hull form

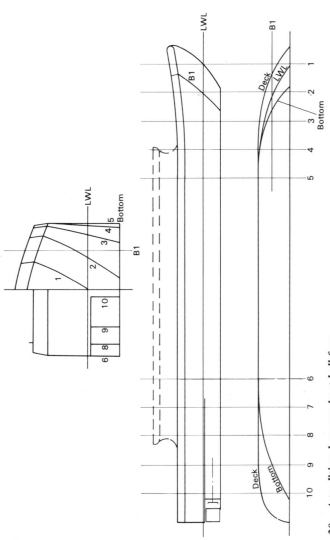

20 A traditional narrow boat hull form

Lines drawings

The eight lines drawings in Figures 13 to 20 show in detail the shape of the different types of hull form mentioned in this chapter. Most of the drawings are very similar to actual cruisers. Each hull is shown viewed from three different angles. The lower drawing is a plan view (looking down on the boat) the middle is an elevation (looking at the boat sideways) and the top drawing is a body plan. This latter drawing shows the hull viewed end-on. The right-hand side shows the forward sections of the boat and the left-hand side the aft sections including the transom. The position of the different sections in the length of the hull are shown on the other two views. On all three views are shown the buttock lines (B1, B2 . . .) water lines (WL1, WL2 . . .) and deck and chine lines. The vertical lines cutting the hull lengthwise create the buttock lines showing up as curves on the elevation. Similarly, waterlines are created by slicing the hull horizontally and these show as curves on the plan view. LWL stands for load waterline and is the normal waterline at which the boat floats.

The points to note on a lines drawing are how deeply the hull sits in the water, and the depth of the keel. The slope of the buttock lines aft dictate how fast the boat can go—the hard-chine forms have horizontal buttocks. Forward sections which are not steeply veed will slam badly. Note the sharpness of the bows at the LWL and the flare of the forward sections above the water, and whether there is a knuckle. Boxy sections give more initial stability than rounded ones but are less seakindly. Sheer lines (the deck line in elevation) vary from sweeping fishing boat style to flat sheers and hogged sheers (running down to the bow). Which is the prettiest?

3   In Rough Water

What makes a good seaboat? How can one tell whether one particular motor cruiser will be better than another? To answer these questions we will look at the behaviour of a boat in rough water in two ways—its ability to take rough water safely, which is called seaworthiness, and its motion in rough water, which is called seakindliness. A boat which is very seaworthy may ride safely like a cork but not be, by any means, seakindly. A seakindly craft will ride smoothly and roll gently, but it does not follow that it is therefore seaworthy, in the strict meaning of the word. Most motor cruisers are neither seaworthy nor seakindly when compared with ballast keel sailing yachts. This may be a surprising statement, but after reading this chapter it will be evident that it is generally true.

First, consider seakindliness—the motion to expect in unsheltered waters in light or moderate winds. Most cruising will be done in winds of up to about Force 5 which can still produce quite nasty seas. Above this wind-strength safety becomes more important, and seaworthiness rather than seakindliness vital. For the size of cruiser considered in this book, cruising should not be attempted in unsheltered waters if the wind is stronger than about Force 5. The motion very much depends on the fetch and the direction of heading of the craft relative to the wind and the waves. To understand the behaviour of a boat among waves it is important to examine what waves are, so at this point we shall digress to this subject.

Wind waves

The pattern of waves on the surface of the sea is irregular, the waves being of different heights, and apparently shapes, but

coming predominantly from one general direction. In fact, the
wave pattern is the product of many trains of regular waves
moving either in-phase or out-of-phase with their neighbours
(Figure 21). The key to the mystery is that wave trains of

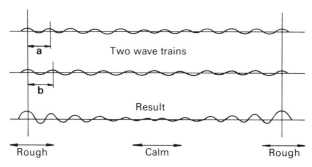

Wavelength **b** slightly greater than **a**

21   This represents a simplified seaway—a more realistic seaway
would consist of many trains of different sized waves

different lengths travel at different speeds (Table 2), the longer
ones travelling faster than and overtaking the shorter ones.
When two crests coincide, the heights are added together,
while if a crest coincides with a trough a relative calm is produced. This phasing 'in' and 'out' means that, in deep water, a

Table 2. Properties of deep water wind waves

Wave length crest to crest ft	Wave speed knots	Time period between crests secs	Approx. max. wave height possible trough to crest ft	Depth at which wave 'feels' bottom ft	Typical areas
5	3	1	1·5	2·5	Reservoir
11·5	4·5	1·5	3	6 ⎫	Sheltered waters, e.g.
20	6	2	4·5	10 ⎭	Solent
46	9	3	7	20 ⎫	Coastal waters, e.g.
82	12	4	10	40 ⎭	English Channel
185	18	6	15	90 ⎫	North Atlantic
328	24	8	20	160 ⎭	
1312	48	16	40	650	South Pacific

single wave cannot be followed by eye very far unless it is a large ocean wave, which may last for a mile or more. But in coastal waters individual crests seem to disappear in quite a short time. This is the reason why it is impossible to surf for long on the crest of a wave in deep water, even if the boat is fast enough to keep up.

The qualification 'deep water' is important, because when waves approach shallow water their speeds are checked and made uniform (dependent now on the depth of water rather than the length of wave) and so the familiar steep and regular beach breakers are formed out of a random wave pattern. The waves begin to 'feel' the bottom when the depth is about half the wave length measured from crest to crest. This is due to the circular motion of the water as the wave passes by. The water itself does not move bodily forward to any great degree, it is the wave shape which moves so rapidly. One can see this with a cork floating on the surface—it rides up and down. Careful observation shows that, in fact, it moves in a circular path. Below the surface this circular motion of 'pieces' of water rapidly becomes smaller and smaller until at a depth equal to about half the wave length the water is practically still.

The wind acting on the surface of the water creates the waves—the longer the distance on which it acts (the fetch) the greater the wave height, up to a certain saturation point. If the wind is offshore, the water close to the beach will be calm and the further away from the beach the rougher the water will become. Thus fetch is a most important point about coastal cruising.

Equally important are the effects of tides and shallow water on wind waves. It is well known that wind against tide produces a steep, dangerous sea, while wind with tide quells the waves. We have also seen that shallow water increases the steepness and height of waves. It can also change the direction of the waves. Suppose a wide, broad-crested wave encounters shallow water at one end of the crest. This part will be slowed, and, like a line of soldiers who, one by one, step into boggy ground, the crest will slew round and head towards the beach. (This is called refraction and is the reason why breakers always approach a beach square on.) The energy of a wave is completely absorbed by a gently shelving beach, but a flat sea-wall will reflect waves just as light is reflected by a mirror. The resulting sea off the sea-wall can be very nasty with waves leaping up and dropping back again.

A wave can only reach a certain steepness before the crest breaks. This can be seen on a gently shelving beach. It can also be seen in deep water in the form of white horses. On a larger scale a source of danger is sudden collapse of a wave crest which has been combined with one, two or more crests of other wave trains.

With coastal cruising it is plain from the foregoing that the fetch of the wind, the direction of tide and the presence of shallow banks, are just as important to the production of a nasty sea as the actual wind strength. The chap who airily says that he took his 20 ft cruiser along the coast from A to B in a Force 8 is either a lucky fool or was able to do so because the wind was offshore.

Response to waves

The motion of a boat is very dependent on the direction in which she is headed relative to wind and wave. Conditions always seem worse when heading into, rather than running with, the waves. The wind feels stronger when heading into it because the apparent wind which one feels is the sum of the speed of the boat and the actual wind strength. Also, the pitching motion is much worse when heading into the waves. Turning off the wind and running with the waves dramatically reduces this motion while the strength of the wind apparently disappears.

If the wind speed is, say, 10 knots and the boat is travelling at 6 knots, heading into the wind the force felt on the face will be 16 knots as against 4 knots running with the wind. The actual pressure of the wind increases with the square of the sum of the speeds, i.e. 16 knots 'feels' 16 times stronger than 4 knots. Rolling will be most noticeable when the boat is broadside on or heading slightly into the waves, and for motor cruisers is usually the most uncomfortable angle of heading, not to say the most dangerous.

But first consider pitching, that is the seasaw motion heading into the waves. In long waves the boat will ride gently up and down the crest (Figure 22). In short waves, shorter than the length of the boat, there will be little or no motion. It is in the intermediate stage where most pitching occurs, i.e. where the wave length is comparable to the length of the boat.

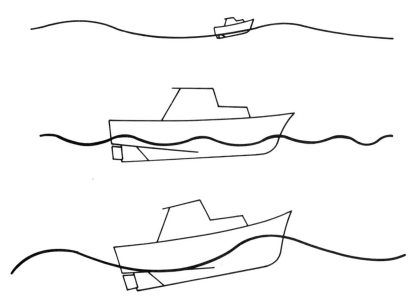

22   *Showing the effect of wave length in relation to the length of the boat*

Another important factor that determines how much a boat will pitch is the time interval between the boat encountering the crest of one wave and the crest of the next. This period of encounter depends on the distance between the crests and the speed of the boat as it heads into the waves. The faster the boat the shorter the period of encounter. If the period of encounter happens to be the same as the natural period of pitch of the boat a large pitching motion can be expected. And if the wave length also happens to be comparable to the boat's length (in fact anything from one to two times the boat's length) extreme pitching is likely. This is called synchronous pitching which is not only wet and uncomfortable but slows the boat appreciably. This phenomenon is common to all hull shapes and there is really nothing that can be done about it at the design stage.

Small motor cruisers have natural pitching periods of around 1 to 2 seconds; that is to say if, in still water, the bows are pushed down and then released the boat will pitch in a rhythmic way and the time taken for the bows to come up and go back down again will be 1 to 2 seconds. To take an example suppose a 20 foot boat with a natural period of 1 second is heading into a sea in which the predominant wave length is 30 ft. The predominant wave period will be 2·4 seconds so at slow speeds there will be no danger of synchronous pitching although the amount of pitch will still be large because the wave length is 1·5 times the boat's length. At 6 knots the period of encounter shortens to 1·33 seconds while at 10 knots it reduces to 1 second—exactly equal to the natural period. At 10 knots the motion will be most severe. The height of waves 30 ft long will be no more than a few feet and such waves can be generated by very moderate winds on a short fetch especially if the tide is running against the waves. Thus synchronous pitching is quite likely to occur in otherwise good sailing weather.

The cure is to go either faster or slower. By going faster the bows will literally have no time to drop in the trough or rise to a crest before their influence is past. Although the actual amount of pitching will be less, obviously the pounding and banging will be very bad. But this is how fast planing boats must be designed to operate.

The same phenomenon of synchronous motion can often occur in the case of rolling. Motor cruisers have roll periods (time to roll from one side to the other side and back again) of around 1·5 to 3 seconds. Wave trains of this period will produce synchronous rolling which, apart from being very uncomfortable, is dangerous. Turning partly into or with the waves will change the period of encounter and the roll will become less. Waves with periods of 1·5 to 3 seconds have lengths of 11·5 to 46 ft. As with pitching, the nasty waves are those with lengths comparable to the boat's own *length*, not breadth as one might suppose. And again much longer or much shorter waves will have little effect on the boat, except when the large ones are very steep or breaking.

This brings us to the third important type of movement— yawing, that is, the slewing round of the stern. In small seas it is only a matter of correction by using the wheel, but in more adverse conditions while running with the sea, it can lead to a

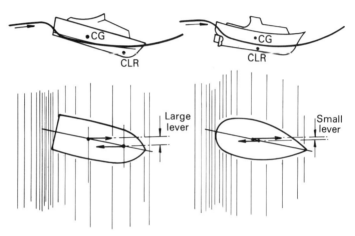

23   *Broaching mechanism. The boat on the left has deep fine bows and a flat wide stern so that the centre of lateral resistance (CLR) is very far forward compared to the centre of gravity (CG). The boat on the right is better off because the stern has deep sections, a keel and large rudder*

broach, that is the stern is slewed round so violently to one side by the crest of a wave, that the boat ends up broadside-on and very vulnerable to capsize by the wave. The sketch (Figure 23) shows how a yawing moment can develop if the boat is not held exactly stern-to to the waves.

Finally, to wind up all the theory, there is the subject of loss of speed in waves, the very appreciable loss which any boat will experience when heading into waves while keeping the throttle opening constant. An 8 knot cruiser (in calm water) may be cut down to 4 knots or less when heading into waves of roughly her own length, especially if she pitches synchronously. One can imagine that severe hobby-horsing will add resistance and cut down the propeller effectiveness. And then, of course, there is the wind drag which has a large effect on cruisers with high cabins.

Seakindliness of displacement hulls

Proportions
Having dealt with the theory we can now get down to applying the results to the performance of different types of motor cruiser in rough water. With seakindliness we are dealing with the degree of motion on a not-too-rough day. And to narrow the field down a stage further, displacement boats will be considered first.

The overall proportions of a boat have a large effect on how much she will roll, pitch and yaw, but changes in hull shape for a given all-up weight and length and breadth have a relatively minor effect. All-up weight, or displacement (both terms have, in effect, the same meaning) is the biggest factor of all. A heavy boat of the same length and breadth as a light one will respond to waves in a less violent way. The sheer inertia to be overcome in throwing a heavy compact object around slows the process and allows a more comfortable ride. The boat will sit in the water rather than on it and behave less like a shallow dish. So for seakindliness a big displacement for the length of boat is a most important factor.

Comparing the displacement (weights) of motor cruisers with ballast-keel yachts (Figure 24) it is obvious that most motor cruisers start off on the wrong foot—they are comparatively very light. Naturally there is some overlap if one takes an ultra-light racing yacht and a heavy trawler-type motor cruiser, but nevertheless the trend is as shown. Surprisingly the band shown for motor cruisers includes both planing boats *and* displacement boats, the diagram being drawn up using the weights of a large number of actual craft. Planing boats are supposed to be light and displacement craft heavy, but in practice most displacement motor cruisers on the market are what I referred to in Chapter 2 as mock displacement shapes, while most planing boats plane by virtue of

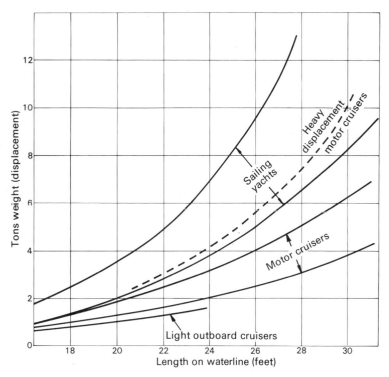

24   Showing how much lighter motor cruisers are compared to sailing yachts

sheer power rather than lightness. The true displacement form will have a weight which, when plotted on Figure 24, will fall just inside the sailing yacht band.

An inboard powered cruiser is usually substantially heavier than an outboard one, because of the difference both in weight of the engine and installation and in design.

Beam in relation to length is not important, and in any case this proportion is fairly uniform amongst all types of small craft. Draught in relation to length, however, is particularly important. Naturally a heavier boat will have a deeper draught, but keel size also comes into it. A deep keel produces more lateral underwater area to resist leeway from strong side winds and also to make steering easier under yawing conditions and to damp roll. When rolling, the keel will swing from side to side, taking with it a large amount of water. This entrained water damps the motion.

Especially under synchronous pitching conditions the bows will come right out of the water and slam back again. Naturally a hull with little draught forward will be inclined to do this more readily than one with a deep draught. By defining draught as the depth of the lowest part of the hull or keel (if fitted) below the waterline, the following table gives an idea of the sort of draughts which constitute 'shallow' and 'deep'.

Length of boat (ft)	20	25	30
Shallow draught (in)	12	18	24
Deep draught (ft)	2·5	3	3·5

Shape

Compared with the overall proportions and weight of a boat, changes in hull shape have a relatively minor effect on the motion, but a major effect on wetness, that is to say, how much water comes onto the deck or into the cockpit. Low freeboard will make a wet boat and lack of freeboard is rarely found in modern motor cruisers. But apart from solid water coming aboard, as soon as water is flung around below gunwale level a strong wind can whip heavy spray aboard. The water is prevented from climbing up the sides or fanning out in a plume from the bows by flare, or a spray rail or knuckle. (See Figure 25.) A clinker form is effective as well. The after part of the hull is less likely to be in conflict with the waves so the flare or knuckle can gradually fade out.

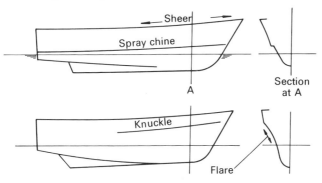

25 *Knuckles and flare*

The phenomenon of synchronisation in roll and pitch is largely unaffected by changes in hull shape, and indeed there is little one can do to stop a boat pitching in any condition. Rolling is a different matter. Steadying sails, bilge keels, the shape of the sections of the hull and ballast can considerably reduce the amount of roll. Bilge keels will not alter the period of roll to any great extent, so the synchronisation problem still exists, but they do damp the actual roll angles (Figure 26).

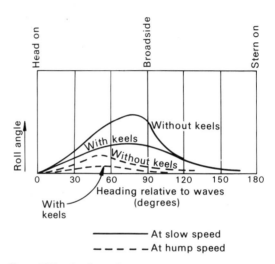

26   *The effect of bilge keels on displacement motor cruisers in rough water*

Bilge keels have to be fairly deep to be effective—a 1·5 in square section will contribute little. Depth is the most important factor and, for a 25 ft boat bilge keels 6 in deep should give the roll reductions shown in Figure 26. With a hard-chine boat the chines themselves act rather like bilge keels. Naturally, a barrel-shaped bottom will hardly resist rolling, whereas a square sectioned one will tend to drag water with it, so there is less need for bilge keels on a hard-chine boat. In any case, bilge keels could not be tolerated on a fast hard-chine boat because of the resistance they produce.

It will be noticed that the faster the boat goes the less the angle of roll. Note that we are still talking of the slower type of boat, in other words speeds up to 7 or 8 knots. It is very noticeable that when stopped, or at speeds up to 4 or 5 knots (speed:length ratios of up to 1·0), a boat rolls much more heavily, particularly broadside-on, than when she is running at speeds approaching the hump. At these higher speeds the boat stiffens up and rolls less, but pitches more. This is one reason why over-powering a displacement sea-going craft is not a bad thing. The fast round-bilge hull is also favourably affected in this way.

The effectiveness of steadying sails depends on the sail area in relation to the size of boat. A ballast-keel sailing boat will hardly roll at all, even broadside on to steep waves, by

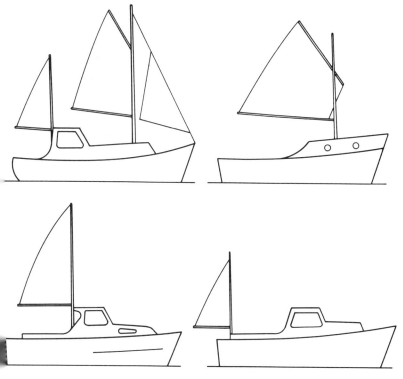

27 Steadying sails. The two top arrangements would provide some propulsion, the one lower left would steady only and the one bottom right would be ineffective for steadying but would give a slight benefit on steering

comparison with a motor boat. The wind pressure on the sails heels the boat over to a steady angle. This heeling moment and the corresponding righting moment of the ballast keel are much larger than the rolling moment which the waves can impart to the hull.

A steadying sail cannot be nearly so effective as this, especially in light winds, but is nevertheless well worth having. Figure 27 shows some varieties of sail areas down to a small mizzen which really has little more than a psychological effect (although it does also look pretty). The larger the sail area the heavier must be the ballast fitted in the bilges to compensate for the heeling effect of the wind. With a small area such as a mizzen, ballast is usually unnecessary. On the other hand ballast equal to 10 per cent of the weight of the boat will allow a fair spread of sail.

Ballasting is a more difficult subject—it can sometimes make matters worse but, generally speaking, the addition of solid ballast in the bilges of displacement cruisers has a beneficial effect. The boat will be more stable and heavier, but there is a chance that she may become too stiff. That is to say, the rolling motion among waves may be very short and sharp. This is more likely to happen with larger boats, upwards of 30 ft, and with round-bilge craft which lack damping devices such as keels and bilge keels. To give a noticeable effect, the weight of ballast has to be at least 10 per cent of the weight of the boat.

At this point it would be useful to pause and consider an ideal displacement cruiser built purely for seakindliness. She would be heavy, as heavy as the true displacement line shown in Figure 24. She would have a deep draught and the hull would be all curves. Bilge keels and steadying sails would reduce roll, while a sweeping sheer, flare and a knuckle would keep the bows high and dry. Some would say that a double-ended hull or canoe or cruiser stern would make a more seakindly craft, but I would say that as far as roll and pitch are concerned a transom stern, providing it is not too broad, is just as good. Perhaps in terms of seaworthiness a pointed or canoe stern is better, as we shall see later.

Traditional hull shapes are often similar to those just described—fishing boat shapes, lifeboat shapes and particularly the familiar clinker style. Clinker construction in timber leads to a pleasing, well-proportioned shape, which has the qualities of seakindliness mentioned so far, together with in-built spray strakes. Single or double chine steel craft also usually make good seaboats because a steel hull is compara-tively heavy and the chine line sweeps deep into the water amidships giving a good bilge keel effect.

Light shallow vee chine hulls powered for displacement speeds are the worst hull form one could choose as regards seakindliness. Such a hull will respond to every little wave, while the flat sections at the bow will slam down when pitching. Far better is the round bottom of even a light displacement shape. Both shapes will be much improved by the addition of a substantial amount of solid ballast, particularly if the boat is outboard powered.

Seaworthiness

Under this heading will be discussed the safety of the boat rather than the motion in waves. The most seaworthy motor cruiser will be stable and strong, a completely watertight 'envelope', and have dual means of propulsion and a means of stopping—an anchor and chain. A seaworthy boat is really one which has all the necessary safety equipment from a bilge pump to a set of lifejackets. Mechanical propulsion is always liable to break down so two independent engines, an auxiliary sail arrangement or an emergency outboard are part of the meaning behind the term seaworthiness. Watertight integrity, strength and stability are necessary in the basic design of a boat. A large open cockpit draining to the bilges may be engulfed by a breaking wave, causing the boat to founder. An open cockpit also considerably reduces the chances of the boat recovering from a very large angle of roll. Once water comes over the gunwale, stability diminishes rapidly. As far as seaworthiness is concerned, a boat is only as strong as its weakest part. Forward facing windows or flimsy hatch covers are often these weak points rather than the hull itself, which is usually the last thing to break up, unless the boat goes aground and is pounded by waves.

The ideal cruiser for seaworthiness would have no cockpit (or only a small one draining overboard through large outlets), small windows and strong hatches, and be stable to an angle of at least 90°, apart from having twin engines and all the necessary equipment. The boat would be like a cork—water would not be able to enter the hull nor could the sea turn her over. Of course I have just described a lifeboat. But a lifeboat is built for a very different purpose from a motor cruiser. Something has to be sacrificed when designing a motor cruiser to give good accommodation and to keep the price down. In time the wise skipper realises the vulnerable aspects of his craft and turns head-on to the worst waves and throttles back, or at least he avoids the worst situation, that is broadside-on to the waves. He also does not intentionally go out in very rough water.

A seaworthy boat is not necessarily a heavy one. So long as she floats, and floats the right way up, she will be safe—although the motion may be violent. There is always the proviso that the propeller must not keep coming out of the water when the boat pitches madly. Outboard-powered boats and boats with pointed sterns are inclined to do this. The loss of thrust is considerable as there is a delay before the air entrained in the propeller is lost. This is an argument in favour of transom-sterned hulls, because the propeller is fully covered and the axis of pitch is further aft. The weight and buoyancy of a transom-sterned hull are rather more aft than forward of amidships especially if the bow lines are fine, so the up and down motion at the stern when pitching is less. A double-ended boat will pitch equally forward and aft. The shapes shown in Figures 4c and 4d will be more prone to propeller emergence than the shapes in Figures 4a and 4b, or planing hulls.

On the other hand, a wide transom in conjunction with fine bows is liable to broach in a following sea. It will be appreciated from Figure 23 that a hull with deep fine bows and an easily swung, shallow, keel-less stern will be more liable to broach than a hull with a deep keel, large rudder and buoyant bows. As soon as the wave has swung the stern a little to one side the inertia of the boat as a whole, still travelling in the same direction, will tend to trip the craft further sideways and eventually broadside-on. Hence if the centre of gravity of the boat is further forward, so much the better. Transom-sterned hulls often have little keel and a centre of gravity more aft than forward, so generally these shapes are more liable to broach than a double-ended or canoe sterned hull.

Waves sufficient in size to broach a boat are much longer than the length of the boat. After all, a 20 or 30 ft long wave can only be a few feet high. It is the longer, faster waves which are a problem. From Table 2 it is evident that waves over, say, 50 ft long are potentially dangerous and these waves are faster than 10 knots. In a powerful boat one might surf as fast as the wave or faster, but the rougher the sea the more dangerous this becomes until one is forced to drop below the wave speed. In many fast craft the rudders are then too small to be effective, and bursts of power are necessary to check the tendency to broach. A sea-anchor dragged astern can allow more engine revs and better steerage without an increase in speed.

Without power, most cruisers will lie broadside-on to the sea and will wallow and roll frighteningly. And, unlike a sailing boat, there is no easy way to heave-to, i.e. make the bows point partly into the wind. It is the relative distribution of areas upon which the wind acts and the distribution of the underwater areas resisting the drift to leeward that dictate how she lies. A tall cabin aft and a low profile forward, together with little keel aft but a deep draught forward will make the boat weathercock bows into the wind. Most cruisers are the other way round to this but not sufficiently to make the boat lie stern-to-wind. A mizzen sail is very useful from this point of view and it also helps steering at low speeds.

Planing boats

So far, only displacement or low-powered craft have been considered. Now is the time to look at fast craft in rough water.

When heading into waves at 30 knots the hull will meet crests at a far greater frequency than when travelling slowly.

The all-important period of encounter will be about 0·25 to 0·5 second for waves of 10 to 20 ft in length, compared with the probable natural period of the boat of 1 to 2 seconds. The craft will be running above her critical speed and so the bows will have no time to drop into the trough between crests. Even heading downwind, the speed of these smaller waves (4 to 6 knots) is small in comparison with the speed of the boat so the period of encounter will not alter very much. It is as though the small waves are stationary like the bumps and hollows on a road surface. The boat is thus like a car running along a rough road. Indeed the motion of a fast small boat is rather like that of a car—sharp and choppy—but less softened and rather more akin to a wooden cart with iron-shod wheels. In larger waves the chance of synchronisation of the period of encounter and natural period becomes greater. For instance, heading into 80 ft long waves the period of encounter at 20 knots would be 1·5 seconds. If a few consecutive waves of this length are met one can visualise that the pitching motion will be extremely violent and the boat would probably dive straight into the face of the second or third crest. In conditions like these, of course, one is forced to slow down.

In short seas a planing boat will seem to a bystander to ride level with little actual motion, whereas a displacement boat may be rolling or pitching very noticeably. On closer inspection, the crew of the planing boat will be subject to a continual rattle from small waves, and thumps and bangs from large ones as successive significant crests are hit. Accelerations on board can be high and if you suffer from 'back' trouble it is usually advisable not to buy a planing boat! In increasingly rough seas there comes a point when the motion and slamming are so violent that the throttle must be closed and eventually planing abandoned. The forces on the hull bottom are enormous, but it is usually the crew who give in first, particularly with modern GRP cruisers.

Generally, the shallower the vee of the bottom the harder the ride. Spray strakes, some people say, give a harder ride. This may or may not be true, but it is certainly a fact that the real deep vee (Figure 19) is softer riding than the older low-chine, shallow vee hulls. The faster the boat goes the more likely it is to leave the water partially or entirely. Upon re-entering, the force of the impact on surfaces of the underwater hull depends on the angle of the surface to the water. A flat pancake landing is obviously the worst. Re-entry will occur to varying degrees along the whole length of the boat and the higher the speed:length ratio the farther aft will slamming forces occur. At speed:length ratios over 4 or 5 the whole length of bottom will be slamming back into the sea, and so deep vee sections need to be carried right through to the transom—hence the deep vee hull shape. With boats whose top speeds correspond to speed:length ratios of 2·5 to 3·5 (only just planing) there is little likelihood of the aft portion leaving the water, and flatter sections aft are permissible. In fact, flat after sections are desirable for easy planing and low resistance (see Chapter 2).

At these lower planing speeds there is basically a choice between a hard-chine and a fast round-bilge form. The latter is the better for seakindliness and, with a deep keel and large rudder and a generally 'displacement' shape, this hull is also better when stopped or going slowly. The fast round-bilge form has necessarily very fine underwater lines forward and, to avoid plunging deep into head or following seas, it needs to have very wide, flared (and thus buoyant) bows above the waterline. Good rake of stem, sheer and flare will give this buoyancy. Wetness is much reduced by a spray strake or chine running just above the static waterline. There are few cruisers on the market with fast round-bilge hulls. Builders tend to choose the ubiquitous hard-chine form, so that with different engines a greater speed range can be offered. This is a pity because the fast round-bilge form gives the best of both worlds—speeds greater than displacement boats, without the jarring harsh ride of planing boats. Also, handling is so much easier at lower speeds.

The possibility of broaching in following seas is much greater with planing hulls and at higher speeds. The shallow vee hull, especially if lacking a keel and fitted with small rudders, is markedly prone to broach, and this older type of hull did give hard-chine boats a bad name. The constant, medium deadrise or deep vee hulls are much better because they have a deeper draught aft and usually a more cut-away forefoot.

Deep vee hulls have less stability at rest because of the lesser breadth at the waterline, and they also tend to be tender at high speeds when running on the apex of their bottoms. This results in an angle of loll if the crew are all on one side, or if there is a strong side wind. From several points of view the medium vee constant deadrise hull is the best at present for family cruisers.

Seaworthiness will really matter only when the sea is too rough for planing. The open cockpit danger is there and also the possibility of broken windows or hatch covers. Stability cannot be gained by the use of ballast, except water ballast (which is hardly ever used). A deep vee hull will have more deeply immersed propellers but be more unstable initially. At larger angles, however, the flared sides will give a good righting moment. Whether a deep vee boat is inherently more seaworthy than a shallow vee one is debatable, as seaworthiness depends on keeping out the water, remaining upright and having proper equipment on board. Planing boats are usually said to be less seaworthy than displacement boats, but within each category one could find exceptions. Nevertheless, the truly all-weather RNLI lifeboat is definitely displacement-shaped!

4 Cabin and Cockpit

A cabin, however small, considerably extends the possibilities of the use of a boat, particularly for a family. It can become a miniature house, catering for basic physical needs, turning a boat into a cruiser—a mobile floating home—rather than a day boat. The cabin can be fitted forward, amidships, aft, over all the hull, or split into two, one cabin forward and one aft. With each arrangement, apart from the 'all-over' type, one can have a large cabin and therefore small cockpit, or a small cabin and large cockpit. Which to choose depends on how many people are to sleep aboard, and for how long. The fisherman might tolerate sparser accommodation, in order that the cockpit can be as large as possible. It all depends on your requirements and inclination to rough it, apart, of course, from price.

Consider the virtues and vices of the different possible cabin positions. The usual layout is a forward cabin and an after cockpit. The space in the cabin is augmented by the space under the foredeck and the bunks can extend right up to the stem, the occupants lying head aft. Even without a windscreen, the helmsman and passengers are sheltered to some extent from the elements, especially the wind. It is easier to produce a boat which looks right if the cabin is forward.

For inland waters this layout is not the logical choice. The attractions of such mill-pond cruising are tranquillity and scenery. Seated passengers cannot see forward, and whether the boat is inboard, outboard or outdrive powered the cockpit is the noisiest part of the boat. A forward cockpit arrangement overcomes these snags, but unfortunately introduces others. Steering from a forward position is more difficult because one cannot tell so easily what the aft end of the boat is doing, for example when entering a lock. Traditional Thames river cruisers and some modern inland cruisers have a forward

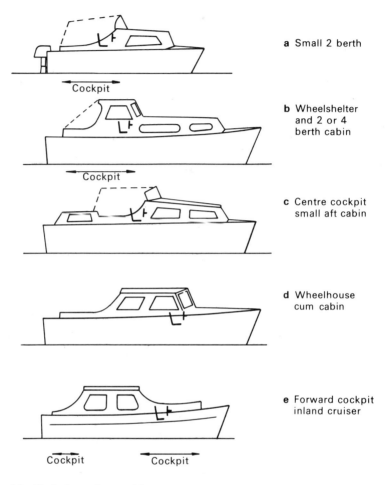

a Small 2 berth

b Wheelshelter
and 2 or 4
berth cabin

c Centre cockpit
small aft cabin

d Wheelhouse
cum cabin

e Forward cockpit
inland cruiser

28   Variations of general layout

cockpit, the latter with a windscreen and sliding top and sides
which turn the cockpit into a cabin for the night. Otherwise
the cockpit space and the space under the foredeck is wasted
as regards accommodation. Whether the helm is situated in
the forward cockpit or not, handling the forward lines and
fenders is much easier from a forward cockpit rather than
a foredeck; one can also walk through the cabin to reach
the bows rather than clamber around the side-decks. The

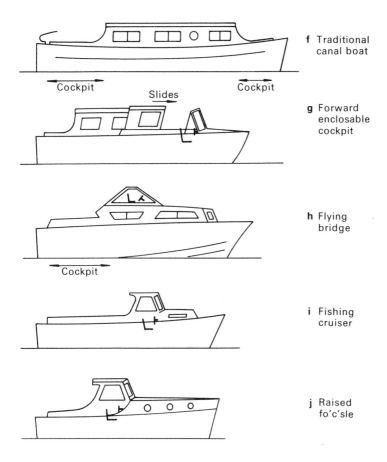

f Traditional
canal boat

Cockpit   Cockpit

Slides

g Forward
enclosable
cockpit

h Flying
bridge

Cockpit

i Fishing
cruiser

j Raised
fo'c'sle

traditional British canal cruiser has a small forward cockpit
and a larger one aft. One never needs to walk around the sides
of the cabin, so the width of the side-decks can be minimal
giving the greatest possible space in the cabin.

Modern GRP inland cruisers (with a few notable exceptions) have a forward cabin arrangement. The reason for this
is probably because the boat builders want to be able to offer
their boat as being suitable for use both inland and on the sea.

This has led to a drab sameness of 20 ft GRP inland cruisers, the monotony of style being accentuated by a near-uniform colour scheme of white hull and blue cockpit cover.

Centre cockpit and aft cabin

For sea work a forward cabin is really unavoidable, and a wheel shelter or even a completely enclosed steering position is most welcome. A centre cockpit arrangement may capture the best of both worlds, especially with an outboard or out-drive engine. The after cabin is then between the engine noise and the cockpit. On such a boat an inboard engine is usually fitted underneath a raised sole, so the helmsman and passengers are sitting high and enjoying a good view; this arrangement is favoured for Norfolk Broads cruisers. Splitting the accom-modation has its advantages if children are aboard, because they can have their own cabin and go to bed early, but this means that the main cabin is smaller. An open plan layout in one big cabin does give an air of spaciousness, which is desirable when living aboard for more than the odd night.

Nevertheless a separate cabin is an increasingly popular trend. Being used purely for sleeping it can be small and often the bunks can be extended forward underneath the cockpit sole, thus reducing the actual length of the cabin to something less than 6 ft. Another idea sometimes seen, which enables an extra two berths to be crammed in, is a separate cabin tucked under a raised bridge deck. The headroom in such a cabin is low and, in fact, one can only crawl in, lie down and go to sleep (see the Fjord 21).

Steering position and engine

The helmsman's position is usually in the cockpit, whether this is forward, amidships or aft. Alternatives are to put the helmsman in the cabin, and in fact make the cabin a wheel-house with large forward windows, or to put him on top of the cabin in a flying bridge arrangement. The trouble with the wheelhouse/cabin arrangement is that the helm has to be rather too far forward for ease of steering, unless one accepts a long, wasteful foredeck. On the other hand, a separate cabin can possibly be arranged under the foredeck on larger craft. If a duplicate outside steering position is fitted then one has an arrangement suited to all weathers. The flying bridge clears the accommodation or cockpit of the helmsman's position and gives the helmsman an excellent view, but it does add top weight and windage, and also access must be by a ladder. Particularly when running the boat single-handed, climbing up and down a ladder makes coming alongside or picking-up a buoy that much more difficult. Naturally one is exposed to the elements up there—there is little chance of rigging anything other than a windscreen.

On boats up to about 23 ft in length, an inboard installation will obtrude into the layout. Sometimes the engine box obstructs the entrance to the cabin or creates rather narrow walkways on each side. Sometimes it is used as a table. The best arrangement is where the engine is fitted beneath the cockpit sole which can only be done on larger boats. The great advantage of an outboard or outdrive is that it does not intrude into the boat. An outdrive is usually tucked under a bench seat across the transom completely out of the way. In some respects an outboard takes up more room than an outdrive because the last 2 ft or so of the boat has to be taken up by a well to allow the motor to tilt up.

The so-called fishing cruiser is usually just a motor cruiser fitted with a cabin having only two berths and perhaps a toilet and a cooker. Such a boat can be a perfectly satisfactory cruiser for more than two people. A canopy will turn the cockpit into another cabin for the night, especially if there is a wheel shelter, because then the canvas will be held higher; folding hoops will also do this. Some cruisers claimed as being 2/4 berth or 4/6 berth do, in fact, have this arrangement. It entails stowing mattresses and sleeping bags somewhere in the cabin during the daytime to prevent them getting wet. Apart from this snag there is not a great deal against the idea, providing the cockpit cover is put up before the dew falls in the evening. A fishing cruiser is naturally cheaper than the version with a larger cabin, so one can buy a bigger boat for the same money, which is always advantageous from the point of view of cockpit space and seaworthiness.

Headroom and access

Cruising demands a boat which offers berths, a toilet and a cooker, but equally important as these obvious items is stowage for all the gear, clothes, food etc. Even a 30 ft boat gives a very small amount of living space, compared with the amount to which we are accustomed ashore, so the maximum use must be made of the length, breadth and depth of the hull. Pointed sterns, long aft decks and wide side decks are wasteful of space.

Headroom and access are two very important aspects to consider—both are virtually fixed once you have bought the boat. There is always conflict in the design of a boat between having full headroom in the cabin and both spoiling the looks of the craft and adding too much windage and top weight. Below 23 ft in length it is rare to find full headroom, except with canal cruisers where stability and windage are of lesser importance. But it is fairly important to be able to stand up somewhere in the boat—to straighten the backbone or pull up a pair of trousers—otherwise a sense of claustrophobia tends to creep in. A wheel shelter is very useful for this, because even a 19-footer will then have standing headroom at one place in the boat with the cockpit cover up.

By 'access' is meant access into or through the cabin—into the toilet compartment and around the engine box. Awkward steps, ledges, sharp corners, narrow doors and fixed tables in the centre of the cabin are instances of poor access. Legs can get bruised on the corner of the engine box, heads bashed on the top of the door frame or cabin beams, or bare toes stubbed on seat supports. If there is only one narrow passageway into the cabin, that is bad enough, but when the cooker and sink are situated to one side of the entrance it can be infuriating for the cook. The ideal arrangement is for the galley to be set in its own separate space so that the cook stands out of the passageway.

Children aboard demand certain considerations. A high coaming around the cockpit is one feature, a separate cabin is another. A table, especially in a dinette arrangement, enables them to be kept busy, perhaps drawing and out of the way on a wet day. With children aboard ample storage spaces are even more important.

Cabin layouts

On cruisers up to about 20 ft in length, the cabin is usually only long enough to enable a berth to be fitted on each side forming a vee in the bows, with perhaps a toilet compartment and a cupboard with space on top for a cooker (Figure 29). Above about 23 ft the cabin can be split into two parts with two berths in each. The dinette arrangement copied from cara- vans is often used on boats of this size to compact the overall length of the cabin (Figure 30). During the day the dinette forms a table with athwartships seats, by night it can be used as a double bed by lowering the table onto a ledge on the edge of the seats and completing the bed area with a fitted cushion. The galley can then be opposite the dinette. The dinette arrangement has its snags. It is good for meals but not so comfortable for just sitting; it is also rather cramped for four. The galley being opposite means that the washing-up is con- spicuous after a meal.

The more traditional style of berth/seat layout (Figure 31) features bunks to port and starboard with a drop leaf table in the centre. The snag with this is that walking through the cabin is difficult, especially with the table leaves up. Also the galley area must be aft or forward of the two berths, so that the cabin has to be that much longer than if the dinette arrangement is fitted.

The less common cabin/cockpit arrangements shown in Figures 28 d, e, f and g give scope for different cabin layouts. For instance, because the traditional British canal cruiser is long and narrow, the accommodation can be split into sleeping cabins and a separate saloon and the galley area can be in a compartment of its own, as can the toilet and shower.

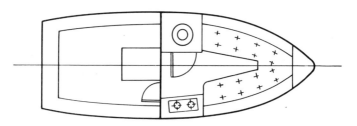

29   *Simple 2-berth layout*

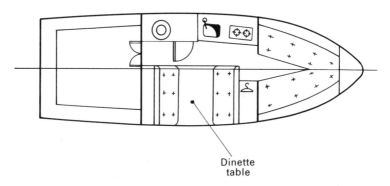

Dinette
table

30   *Common 4-berth open plan arrangement with dinette*

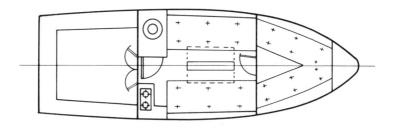

31   *4-berth layout with settee berths and a small forward cabin*

This separation of living, cooking and sleeping areas, which is only possible on boats longer than perhaps 23 ft, is in direct contrast to the open plan style which has crept in from America. With a 25-footer, for example, one can have either two separate cabins, or even three separate areas with the all-enclosed arrangement of Figure 28g, or one large open plan cabin with the berths more or less head to foot. Which to choose is entirely a matter of taste.

Berths
If the cabin has sufficient headroom it is possible to have upper and lower berths. The upper berth folds down and forms a backrest to the lower during the day. Thus four berths can be fitted into a cabin only a little more than 6 ft long. The snag is that the occupants cannot sit up in bed to read, and if they do sit up suddenly in the night they will bang their heads. The flare of the bows sometimes allows a vee-shaped shelf, wide enough to be called children's berths, to be fitted. The edge of these bunks forms the backrest to the berths/seats below. A curtain is sometimes fitted to the upper berths so that the children can go to sleep earlier in the evening, with the main cabin light on. Another innovation concerns the vee-shaped berths commonly fitted in the forward end of the boat. These can be made more comfortable if there is a triangular-shaped cushion section which fits between the berths.

Berths on boats tend to be very narrow and it is easy to fall out when turning over during the night, particularly when sleeping on the outside of a dinette. Leeboards, either wood or canvas, help but they are rarely fitted. (They are quite easy and cheap to add later, however.) The important features of a berth are its length, width at the shoulders and the thickness of the cushion. Sleeping bags and pillows are more practical than sheets and blankets. I find 22 in width at the shoulders and 3 in thickness the bare minimum, while an extra 3 in of width and 1 inch of thickness make a big difference, but these figures and the actual length of the berth are matters of personal choice. A berth 6 ft 3 in long should suit most people, but if you happen to be 6 ft 4 in tall . . .

Berths often taper, which does not matter providing the

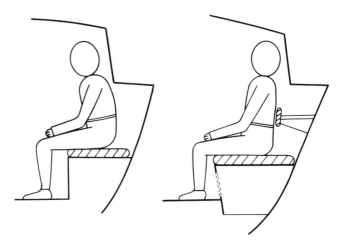

*32 Good and bad seating arrangements. Note also the sides of the
bunks*

width at the shoulders is there. Similarly if the toe-end of the
berth extends under the foredeck, for example, this causes no
discomfort, providing one's feet have 'headroom' to turn over.
Many people, including myself, have slight claustrophobic
tendencies which may come out in a dream during the night.
A cramped cabin, particularly if there is not full headroom,
impresses itself on the mind during the day, giving frightening
dreams in the dead of night, such that one wakes up in a panic,
sits up abruptly and perhaps bangs one's head against a roof
beam. If you are prone to this, then sleeping in the cockpit is
better.

During the day the berths will be used as seats so it is
desirable to have a backrest at the right height (about 9–12 in
above the berth). If the shoulders come up against the cabin
side first, sitting for any length of time becomes most uncomfortable (see Figure 32).

Stowage

On a cruise of more than a day there is a great deal of gear for
which stowage space must be found. There will be food—tins,
packets, boxes, bottles—clothes, sleeping bags, toilet items,
books, cutlery, saucepans and so on. Shelves are useful for

cups, books and bottles, while a cool cupboard is important for such things as cheese, butter, milk and eggs. Storage spaces under the bunks are usually arranged, but often access is through the top of the bunk rather than the side. This means that to get at anything, everything on the bunk, including the mattress, has to be shifted, which is a nuisance and easily avoided by having access through the side. A hanging locker is useful for wet oilskins which, if folded, never dry, or for clothes which will crease if folded. On sea-going boats the cupboards and drawers should have positive means of closing to avoid everything tipping out when the boat rolls heavily. Door catches and 'lift and pull' drawers are the answer. On the same theme, tables and working tops should have fiddles—strips of wood around the edge—to stop things sliding off.

GRP cabins are very unlikely to leak, but cupboards whose backs are formed by the hull itself can collect pools of condensation. This is easily cured by lining the offending piece of hull inside the cupboard. Modern family cruisers usually have plenty of stowage arranged, but cupboards and shelves are easily added by a practical boat owner. Indeed one will never find the perfect boat, and small details and fittings such as shelves, ventilators, hooks and carpet can be added later as use of the boat may show them to be needed. Buying a boat is not like buying a car where one need never add an extra. A boat is not merely something in which to go from A to B—there is always some improvement which can be done to make living aboard a little easier.

Galley

A galley may be just a cooker fixed on top of a cupboard. One can usually specify the type of cooker preferred. The choice is between gas, paraffin and methylated spirits (alcohol). Gas is most common because it is quick, cheap and clean to use. But there is always the possibility of an undetected gas leak eventually causing an explosion or fire. That possibility is remote if the installation of the gas bottle and pipework is correct and if the tap on the gas bottle is always turned off after use. Basically the gas bottle should be stowed well away from engines and batteries and in a watertight box which is itself drained overboard (the gas is heavier than air—thus any leakage will drop to the bottom of the box and thence overboard). The piping should be of seamless copper and run high up in the boat and certainly not in the bilges, and only short lengths of flexible hose should be used to join the copper pipe to the bottle and the cooker. The above elementary rules (basically British Standard Code of Practice) should be observed with any gas appliance—cookers, refrigerators, heaters etc.

Paraffin is also a cheap fuel and comparatively very safe. The main snag is that before vaporisation (and hence cooking) can start, the burners have to be preheated with methylated spirits.

The methylated spirit stove is a little slower, but again very safe and gives off a pleasant smell. Vaporisation is achieved sometimes by directly burning from a kind of convection wick and sometimes by preheating, using a small amount of methylated spirits poured into a tiny tray underneath the burner, so there is again a delay of perhaps a minute or two before the saucepan can be put on the ring.

On seagoing boats the cooker should have fiddles to prevent things sliding off. Gimbles are not really necessary on a motor cruiser, because the roll is about the upright rather than a steady angle of list as on a sailing yacht. The area around and above the cooker should be free of anything flammable, for example a curtain or soft lining. It is desirable that the cook has headroom by the cooker to stand up or, failing this, a seat. Scandinavian boats often have the galley situated in the cockpit, albeit inside the wheel shelter. One can envisage drawbacks but it does leave the cabin free of cooking smells, and may be less cramped for the cook. A working area is useful but the table top can double for this purpose. A sink with a freshwater tap completes the galley on small boats, although this can be dispensed with by buying a plastic washing-up bowl and a plastic water container and doing the washing-up in the cockpit. Some sinks are so small that one can hardly get a plate in, and the water pump or tap-cum-pump frustratingly slow. An electric pressure pump system is a further refinement.

For a week's cruise, a 5-gallon container of water is hardly sufficient reserve—it will have to be topped up every day, which may be inconvenient. Anything larger becomes too heavy to be readily portable, so a built-in tank is the solution. This can be a GRP tank moulded into the hull, or one of stainless steel, galvanised steel or rubber.

The toilet

The choice lies between the so-called sea-toilet which discharges directly overboard, and a chemical toilet—the simplest of which is a bucket with seat. There is also the re-circulating, flushing type of chemical toilet. For inland waters it is usually compulsory to use a chemical toilet. Sometimes a toilet compartment is not fitted—the toilet is installed underneath one of the bunks. Naturally this arrangement has its disadvantages, and for a cruising boat it is not practical. Toilet compartments naturally cannot be very spacious and in many cases it is necessary to pull one's trousers down before backing in! A dummy run quickly finds out the faults of a toilet area when choosing a boat. In many layouts the compartment is fitted just inside the cabin and often necessarily adjacent to the galley and food cupboard, which is not the ideal place. A position in the forepeak under the foredeck is the most remote and private, but it takes up a large amount of a space that could be utilised

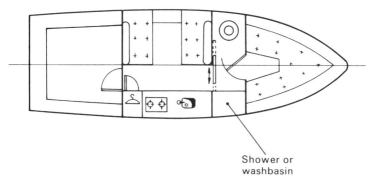

Shower or washbasin

33   4-berth layout with enclosable 'bathroom'

for two berths. Another arrangement sometimes seen, which is perhaps the best compromise, is an enclosable space between the forecabin and the main saloon as in Figure 33. A wash-basin can be fitted, or a shower, or even both, so a complete bathroom is achieved with access from both cabins during the night. A seacock should be fitted to a sea-toilet so that when the boat is left for the week it can be turned off. A leak in some part of the toilet does not then sink the boat.

Fitting-out

A cabin can appear warm and cosy, white and clinical, or just plain austere. Scandinavian boats usually have warm and homely-looking cabins achieved by soft-textured orange-coloured bunk cushions and carpets, together with soft linings over the deckhead and boat sides and teak-faced plywood joinery. The addition of a carpet and curtains makes a huge difference to any cabin. Light colours are best, unless the window area is particularly large. Apart from giving a more homely feeling, curtains and a carpet will reduce the noise level with the engine running and the cabin will sound less hollow when the engine is stopped. Although plastic laminate surfaces are easy to clean, too great a use of this material does tend to make a cabin look clinical. Varnished mahogany, if used too extensively, can make a cabin dark and sombre. The best cabins use the approprite materials in the right amounts.

Insulation and linings can also transform the looks and feel of a cabin. Condensation is a problem on small boats, but it can be minimised by insulation and ventilation. Condensation is formed particularly during autumn nights, or on wet days with everybody cooped up in the cabin, or when cooking. Thermal insulation will reduce the heat transfer from the cold air outside to the warmer air inside. The temperature of the inside surfaces will then be closer to the temperature of the air in the cabin, and there will be less tendency for condensation to form. The cabin will also be warmer on a cold night and cooler on a hot day. Steel and aluminium boats are bad from both these aspects. On the other hand thick timber is very good. Plywood and GRP come somewhere inbetween. Normally a foam-backed vinyl cloth acts as sufficient insulation and it also acts as an attractive lining.

Lack of ventilation in the cabin will cause mildew to form on cushions, lifejackets and the deckhead, and will make clothes feel damp. This will be more noticeable towards the end of the season when the air temperature drops sharply during the night. The cabin will feel damp and smell musty, and on wooden boats lack of ventilation is an open invitation for rot to start. Even a small cabin should have at least two ventilators. A toilet compartment should have one and there should also be one over the galley. Rarely is ventilation designed-in in the form of ducts in the bilges leading to ventilators on deck. However, there are many types of roof ventilators available which effectively let in a useful amount of air yet keep out water. Having got fresh air circulating around the cabin it is important that the air should have a chance to circulate behind linings and through lockers. For instance, where a lining is in the form of thin plywood there should be gaps along the edges to promote air flow between the lining and the hull. This is vital in a wooden boat where pools from condensation are a sure cause of rot and, in a steel boat, rust. In GRP boats condensation is likely to cause damp clothes inside a locker, or mould and mildew. Large finger holes or slots should be present on all lockers to provide some air flow.

Floor coverings range from bare wood to carpet and vinyl sheeting. Vinyl flooring is easy to clean and the backed varieties fairly warm and soft underfoot, but carpet is, to my mind, the obvious choice. The actual area covered is so small that the cost and cleaning problems are of little importance.

Cabin lights tend to be rather dim, 12 or 18 watt bulbs being quite normal. The maximum wattage of the bulbs is strictly limited by the battery capacity. There must be sufficient power left in the battery—after the drain of an evening's lighting—to start the engine in the morning. The smallest battery likely to be installed is one of about 40 amp hour, i.e. one amp can be taken for 40 hours, 2 amps for 20 and so on. Burning two 18 watt bulbs will consume 3 amps (12 volt battery), so if this battery is fully charged it will last for 13 hours. During an evening the lights would only be on for perhaps 3 hours. With sensible use more powerful cabin lights can often be fitted, even with the smallest battery capacity. Diesels are equipped with bigger batteries but they require greater starting power, so the spare capacity available for lights is still not very great. One can see the advantages of an alternator which will quickly charge the battery as soon as the engine is started. In the twin-battery arrangement, one battery is fitted for engine starting only and the other for lights etc., so that there is always battery power available to start the engine. Fluorescent lights consume much less electricity but they are expensive and give off the familiar harsh white light.

A large expanse of cabin window is suspect from several aspects. Seaworthiness is compromised even if the glass is toughened, while it can make people feel as if they are in a gold-fish bowl. After all, a cabin is primarily for privacy and shelter. Toughened glass set in aluminium frames is the best and most expensive form of window. Ordinary glass should never be used. Perspex is strong and flexible but it tends to scratch and become opaque rather easily. A Perspex window set in a rubber moulding can be fairly readily punched out and, from the strength point of view, this way of fitting a window should only be used on boats for sheltered waters. A windscreen wiper should act on a glass screen, not one of Perspex. Cleaning a Perspex window should always be done with copious fresh water; salt crystals scratch the surface very badly. A skylight window or glazed hatch will need to be covered up at night to save the crew from being woken at sunrise.

Cabin heaters are improving rapidly. Obviously safety is a prime requirement, but so also is the production of heat without moisture. The burning of liquid fuels, even catalytically, can give rise to a large amount of condensation in the cabin after a few hours. A flue is the answer and for serious cabin heating it is essential. Space for a cabin heater is often difficult to find—it is rarely provided by the boat builders.

An escape hatch in the cabin roof is necessary if the cabin is anything but a small two-berth affair. The engine and the galley are the two most likely places for a fire to start and these are often close to the main cabin entrance—hence the need for an alternative escape route. A hatch is also useful for ventilation. Naturally hatches should be strong with good catches, and be spray and rain tight.

Apart from windows and perhaps hatches all the items mentioned in the above section can easily be added, or improved upon later. It is impossible to find a boat which fits one's requirements exactly, and if the boat builder will not change his specification or if money is tight, then a little DIY work is the answer.

The cockpit

This is the part of the boat in which most of the day-time will be spent. A large cockpit is pleasant, but it can only be had at the expense of cabin space—one has to sort out the priorities. The helmsman's position is very important and this aspect is dealt with in Chapter 10. On inland waters a wheel shelter or inside steering position is unnecessary, unless cruising is contemplated in all weathers. Inland, air temperatures are usually higher and the water more sheltered from strong winds than at sea. Spray is hardly likely to come over the bows. Half the point of cruising inland is denied to a helmsman hiding under a wheel shelter. On the sea it is a different matter, depending, of course, on the cruising area. A cockpit canopy is important to retain bright varnish work and prevent general rusting and decay. If the cover is specially tailored to fit and can be put up and down easily, it may be useful on cold days, or to turn the cockpit into a cabin during the night. The design of a cover is often left as an after-thought and clumsy, time-consuming affairs are frequently fitted. A large cover which has to be taken off completely, folded-up and stowed somewhere is a nuisance, while refitting in a strong wind, with no idea of which end goes where, is even more of a nuisance. Turnbuttons and 'press-the-dot' fasteners make the work harder. They become stiff and rusty in time and the cover may shrink slightly, making it difficult to pull into place. The best cover is one which need only be undone on three of its sides and then folded backwards

or forwards onto its fourth side in a neat heap. Sometimes a
shallow well is provided across the transom for just this purpose. Any hoops should also fold back into the same well. With
a folding cover like this turnbuttons are adequate but, even so,
the material will never be held taut and it will flap in the wind

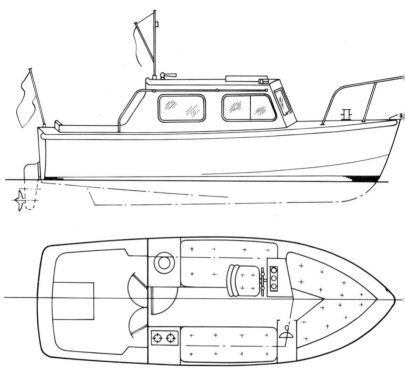

*34   A sea-going 'cabin cum wheelhouse' arrangement making use
of the advantages of an outdrive. Note the large hatch over the
helmsman for sunny days and the double doors opening out into the
cockpit. On a length of 22 ft there is full headroom and 4 berths.
The fast round-bilge hull form gives 11 knots with a 40 h.p. diesel*

and create draughts in the cockpit. Shock cord (elastic cord
$\frac{3}{16}$ or $\frac{1}{4}$ in diameter) threaded through eyelets around the
perimeter of the cover, and pulled down onto hooks screwed
to the boat, will keep the cover taut and allow for slight
shrinkage.

The cockpit sole (the deck) needs to have a non-slip surface. Varnish and GRP are very poor from this point of view. Deal boards tend to swell and shrink and the gaps between the planks allow dirt to fall into the bilges. Plywood is better, but this has to be split into panels to give access to the bilges.

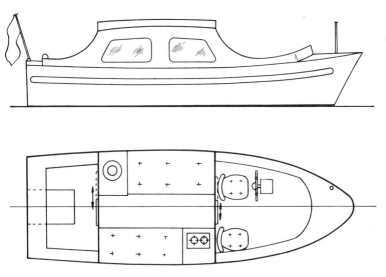

35 A logically arranged 24 ft river or canal cruiser. Note how one can walk through the boat from end to end and the forward seats away from the engine noise. The engine drives through a vee drive or an outdrive and the cabin with full headroom can take two or four berths. The jackstaff aids steering

Finger holes for lifting the panels or boards should not occur over the propeller shaft, in case a child pushes a rope through the hole and entangles it around the shaft. The traditional mahogany cockpit seats are often too narrow to be comfortable and lack a satisfactory backrest. Modern GRP cruisers usually have more ergonomically designed and upholstered seats. With small children aboard, the gunwale needs to be a good height above the top of the seats. With larger unobstructed cockpits such as those found on fishing cruisers, folding canvas chairs intended for gardens are a comfortable alternative to fixed wooden seats. They are cheap and can be moved around to suit the sun and wind direction.

Stowage in the cockpit is needed for fenders, ropes, tools, spare fuel and perhaps lifejackets and the spare anchor. Ideally the lockers should be spray or rain proof with access through the side rather than the top, if the top is a seat. Rather than the locker side dropping vertically down to the deck it should slope inwards to gain toe room when standing close to the locker.

To reiterate a point mentioned earlier, look out for sharp corners, for example on seats and engine boxes. It is so easy to bruise a leg, not once, but several times in the course of a day on board a boat, especially if the craft is rolling about.

A stowage place for a lifebelt is worth considering, as this is an item which needs to be instantly accessible. For sea-going craft a flat area on which to spread a chart is desirable—perhaps the engine box will allow this. Some thoughtful boat builders provide a moulded-in chart area just in front of the helmsman, correctly-sized to take a standard chart. The helmsman's position is discussed more fully in Chapter 10.

5 Construction

Which is the best material for a boat hull? Is it GRP, as most boats seem to be made of this material? The GRP salesman will undoubtedly say it is but, likewise, the builder of a wooden, steel or concrete hull will claim that his particular material has great merits. It is often glibly said that GRP is maintenance-free—among other things—but this is not really true in practice. The material has its own problems to which the owner will have to attend, in the same way that wooden hulls need scraping and painting. But it is true to say that a GRP boat, especially if the cabin and decks are also of GRP, will require far less maintenance than a wooden boat. Just what maintenance is required will be discussed in detail later.

Most boats being built today are of GRP, all the other possible materials taking very much second place. To my mind this is only in part because GRP is a very suitable boat-building material, the other factor being that it is a very convenient material for the boat-building industry. It lends itself to production-line techniques and building the hull is no longer a time-consuming job for craftsmen. Each hull is precisely the same shape, so that bulkheads and interior work can be made independently knowing they will fit. A hull can be peeled off a mould every day or two, and the labour involved is often said to be unskilled, although now that experience in moulding techniques has been gained, it is clear that to produce a good moulding the laminators employed need to be trained in their special skills.

The second commonest material is wood. In terms of the number of boats afloat there are probably just as many wooden craft as GRP. To someone brought up on wooden craft the thought of changing over to GRP is often repugnant—to change from a warm, lovely-textured and easily worked material to one that is soul-less, cold and clinical in appearance, is regarded as a retrograde step. I mention these aspects because here is an example of how the choice of a boat not only will, but should, be dictated by aesthetic as well as technical considerations.

There are people who say that a wooden craft is a bad buy nowadays or even unsafe, or that a GRP boat tends to shatter when pounding into a rough sea, or that aluminium practically melts in salt water, but tales like these can be ignored. Each material has its advantages and disadvantages and, providing the boat is well built and then suitably maintained, any recognised boat hull material will give years of satisfaction. So if the boat that catches your eye happens to be made of steel, then there is no need to be put off by the possibility of rust. Each material has its drawbacks, but each has its attractions and it is easy to convince oneself that steel, for example, has its appeal, especially when one knows that the rust problem can be overcome with epoxy coatings and other modern treatments. Steel is strong and makes a good, heavy displacement hull. And consider the large number of small ships there must be around the world constructed of steel plate only slightly thicker than that on a small boat . . .

No, if one is free from a prejudice in favour of one particular form of construction then it is easy to convince oneself of the suitability of any of the various materials. On the other hand, if it *must* be a wooden craft or one of glossy GRP, then the best advice is to follow the whim, whatever logic advises.

Far from directing the reader away from or towards any particular material, the following sections merely try to point out the pros and cons, what maintenance will be required, and how to tell whether the hull is well built.

GRP

GRP stands for glass reinforced plastic. GRP construction is a world of its own, completely different to the old traditional boat shed full of wood shavings and sawdust. It is a world that has its own language. Basically, a sheet of glass fibre cloth or mat is laid on a mould and liquid resin is squeezed and rolled into the glass. This forms a single layer which cures (sets) in a few hours, after which successive layers are built up until the required amount of glass and total thickness is achieved. Applying the resin and rolling it into the glass with little rollers is a horrible, sticky, messy and smelly business. Styrene fumes, given off as the laminate cures, are still detectable after several weeks, so a new boat may have a lingering smell. The setting time for the resin depends very much on the temperature inside the shop. Too long a setting time is detrimental to the quality of the moulding, so the temperature is important. Similarly, excessive humidity and dust will reduce the quality, so the first requirements for a good hull moulding are that the boat builder keeps his shed clean, draught-proof and heated.

The skill of the laminators—the people who brush and roll the resin into the glass fibres—determines the quality of each layer. The aim is to squeeze out air bubbles, and prevent the mix being too rich with resin or being too dry. The strength of GRP comes from the glass fibres—the resin itself is structurally very poor and is easily cracked. The purpose of the resin is to bind all the fibres into a homogeneous mass. Naturally the greater the amount of glass incorporated in a laminate the stronger it will be, but this can only be taken so far. Too little resin will make a moulding susceptible to water soakage and delamination, so a compromise has to be struck at a resin-to-glass ratio of about 2·5:1 by weight. This means that the quality of the moulding depends on the degree of control exercised in weighing glass and resin in the shop.

Before the first layer of cloth and resin is put on the mould, a gel coat is applied (after a release agent so that the GRP does not stick to the mould). The gel coat is the vital skin of a GRP hull which stops the ingress of water into the lamination. It is a flexible resin, with the thickness of a coat of paint, but it is this coat which gives that smooth glossy finish, and upon its maintenance depends the appearance and life of the hull. If the gel coat is damaged and not repaired fairly quickly, water will creep into the laminate, destroy the bond between the glass fibres and the resin, and in frosty weather freezing water will gradually crack open the laminate.

For boat building, only certain types of resin and glass can be used. Nowadays the marine materials are well known by boat builders and manufacturers alike—hence such phrases in the boat builders' advertisements as 'Lloyds approved materials'. The glass can be in the form of chopped strand mat (CSM) which is a loosely bound mat of short lengths of glass fibre, or woven roving which is a cloth with much longer filaments of glass, woven like rush matting. There are also cloths such as fine tissue cloth which is sometimes used next to the gel coat or as the last layer to make the inside surface smoother. Chopped strand mat is the most common form because it is the cheapest. Woven roving makes a much stronger laminate (about twice as strong) but if it is used at all it is incorporated near the inner and outside surfaces of the moulding, where its strength does the greatest good.

Of necessity each laminate has to be allowed to gel before the next is put on. The more complete the state of cure the less chance there is of achieving a good bond between the new laminate and the previous one. This is especially so with woven roving laminates where the resin content is less and the rolling and stippling process more difficult. It is good practice, therefore, to alternate woven roving with CSM. Thus there are two basic types of lay-up; first, all CSM with perhaps a layer of scrim cloth or tissue on the outside to reinforce the gel coat, and second, the bulk of the lay-up being CSM with one or two layers of woven roving near the surface to increase the strength. Few boat hulls are made entirely of woven roving —the danger here is that the individual layers may not be properly bonded together possibly permitting delamination later on.

Resin, and the finished laminate, is translucent and slightly green in colour, and if white or a colour is required, a pigment is introduced into the gel coat and perhaps the resin on the first layer. The last layer can also be pigmented to colour the inside surface. Colouring makes inspection during the consolidating (rolling-out) process much more difficult, because air bubbles and so on cannot be seen, so the number of layers actually coloured should be kept to a minimum.

The resin used in boat building is polyester, the alternative—

epoxy—being stronger but too expensive. The mould is a female mould, in other words, the GRP is put on on the inside surface so that the smooth side of the finished laminate will be outside. The female mould is usually of GRP moulded over a wooden male mould or even an actual wooden boat hull. Any imperfections in the female mould will be faithfully reproduced in the outside surface of the laminate.

Practically any hull shape can be made providing it can be pulled out of the mould and curvatures impossible in wooden boats are possible with GRP—sharp double curvature, full rounded bows at the deck, moulded-in bilge keels, rubbing strake flats, anchor recesses in the deck, even a flat area for a compass position. Cabin and interior or cockpit mouldings can have all sorts of ingenious moulded-in features. Even the sink and draining board, cup racks, grab rail flats and so on can be moulded-in. On the other hand, there are some forms which are best avoided with GRP. Flat panels and sharp corners are examples. Compared with wood, GRP is heavy and floppy. For the same thickness, a panel of GRP is only a little stiffer than a panel of plywood or planked timber, but is about three times as heavy. In fact, flexibility is the governing criterion rather than strength. Curvature in a panel increases the stiffness enormously without the need for thickening or stiffening on the inside.

For the designer of a GRP hull the low stiffness is a very important feature of the material. Hard-chine hulls, especially the shallow vee variety, necessarily have large flat panels which, when made of GRP will flex quite alarmingly by hand pressure alone. This is poor design. GRP can bend appreciably without breaking but if there are hard spots about which the material has to bend, cracking and crazing of the surface will eventually occur. A hard spot can be caused by a bulkhead, for instance. At this point the hull is held rigidly and this is the point at which trouble is most likely to occur if the moulding is too thin and light. Particularly for sea-going boats large flat panels in the hull moulding are features of poor design.

Apart from engine bearers most of the stiffening to the hull is achieved by bulkheads, bunks, the deck and side decks etc. In other words, apparently non-structural members, if made of GRP or plywood, can be used to stiffen the hull. They are bonded to the skin and must not be taken out in the course of subsequent DIY work. Simulated clinker construction, knuckles and chines all add stiffness to the hull, so moulding a clinker style is not so silly as might at first be thought.

Sharp corners are very difficult to laminate, actually to force the glass fibres right into the corners. The tip of the corner will be resin-rich and easily chipped. It is worth examining corners on the cabin top, keel and the transom.

Another characteristic of GRP is the poor abrasion resistance. It is easy to scratch and score and it does not take much force to scrape away the protective gel coat and expose the laminations to water attack. Thus it is essential to protect the keel, bilge keels, gunwales and the transom corners with timber rubbing strakes, especially if the craft is to take the ground frequently or is to be used on canals.

The attachment of bulkheads, bunks, engine bearers and so on is usually done by bonding the item in place with strips of cloth or mat and resin. The strength of the bond, especially in 'peeling', depends on the state of cure of the hull. It is best done as soon as possible after the hull is made, but obviously some bonding will be done when the hull is fully cured. The area to be bonded must be abraded and dust free, and again conditions must be warm and dry. Epoxy resins make a good bond. Some examples of connections are shown in Figure 36. In areas such as the keel and chine the number of layers should be increased. One should be able to see this thickening on the inside of the hull.

The joint between the hull and deck is particularly important for both strength and watertightness. The deck moulding is the most important stiffener to the empty hull. A hull moulding straight off the mould is usually weak and floppy, but the deck, when attached, holds the deck line rigid and much increases the torsional rigidity of the hull—the rigidity in twist.

GRP crushes quite easily under the head of a bolt so the load must always be spread by means of washers or wooden or metal pads. Washers should have an outside diameter of at least $2\frac{1}{4}$ times the diameter of the bolt. Unlike fittings on wooden boats, where a bolt can be driven through a tight hole

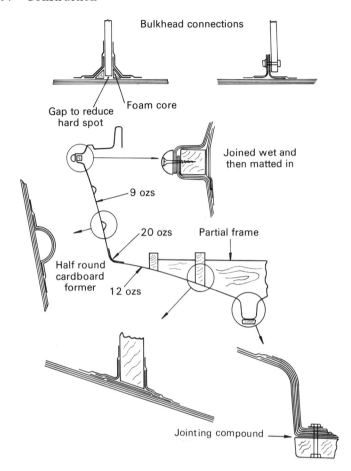

Bulkhead connections

Gap to reduce hard spot

Foam core

Joined wet and then matted in

9 ozs

20 ozs

Partial frame

Half round cardboard former

12 ozs

Jointing compound

36   A section through a GRP hull with typical connection details

and the swelling of the wood relied upon to give water tightness, fittings attached to GRP need a good sealing compound. Bollards, stanchion sockets, seacocks, exhaust fittings all need a good bedding compound. Where large loads will be applied (bollards, for example, or engine bearers) the laminate should be thickened locally.

How to tell a good moulding
This discussion of the problems and pitfalls associated with GRP mouldings will have made it apparent that appreciable

skill is needed in the actual moulding, together with good quality control, as well as the basic factory requirements. It will also be realised that it is impossible to determine the quality of the finished laminate by inspection alone. It is impossible to tell whether the interior layers are dry or full of air bubbles; whether the resin cured satisfactorily in the correct time, or even whether the materials were of the correct quality. The only real way to check on these points is to cut out samples of the moulding and test them in a laboratory. Examination of the cut-outs taken for items such as skin fittings will reveal the thickness of the moulding at those places.

What is possible is to have a look round the factory and see the moulding taking place. The moulding shed should be warm, dry and clean. Hull moulders can get a Classification Societies Approval of their facilities and materials. For instance, Lloyd's 'Approval of Works' means that work was being carried out in the correct temperature using approved methods and materials at the time of inspection. It is by no means a guarantee of good quality but it is a step in the right direction.

Looking at the hull of a finished boat one can examine the smoothness and depth of colour of the gel coat, also looking for fine hair cracks. The inside surface should be reasonably smooth without fibres of glass poking out of the laminate, or runs of resin; these faults are signs of very poor quality. The sharpness of corners and the attachment of fittings can be examined. Fittings bolted on with no washer or plate under the nut show poor craftmanship. If the side of the hull can be flexed appreciably this is a sign of poor design. Where engine bearers and bulkheads are moulded to the hull the connecting angle laminations should be on both sides of the member and substantial in width and thickness. If it looks weak it probably is. The timber used for frames and engine bearers should at least be free of knots. It is also worth looking at the hull/deck joint to see if it looks strong and watertight. On fast planing boats the bottom should be well stiffened with moulded-in frames or longitudinals to take the inevitable pounding.

What thickness should the hull be? It is more meaningful to ask, what is the total weight of glass reinforcement per square foot of laminate? It is the glass which gives the strength. A laminate may typically be made up of gel coat, a layer of 10 oz (per square yard) cloth and then five layers of 1·5 oz (per square foot) CSM, the total weight of glass thus being 8·5 oz per square foot. For some reason woven roving and cloth weights are given in terms of oz per square *yard* and CSM in oz per square *foot*. Boat builders usually give figures for this lay-up and Figure 37 will give a yardstick for comparison. This

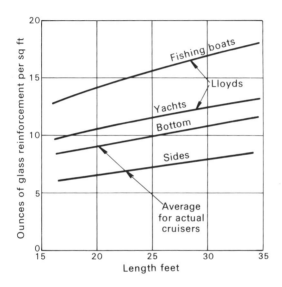

37   *Nominal glass weights for GRP hulls using CSM only.*
Around the keel and chines for instance the laminate will be thickened

diagram is based on the use of CSM only in the lay-up. The use of layers of woven roving will allow some reduction in weight of glass. The required lay-up of a hull also depends on how much stiffening is incorporated, either frames or longitudinals or in-built stiffeners such as the simulated clinker form. The thickness which results from a lay-up of a certain number of ounces of glass depends on the resin:glass ratio and the degree of compaction, but on average it is about 32 oz per inch, or 4 oz per $\frac{1}{8}$ inch.

Having mentioned Lloyd's Approval of Works it is also worth mentioning that a boat can be approved by Lloyd's in respect of the hull moulding, the fitting out, the machinery, or all three, and a certificate issued. This mainly applies to boats over 20 ft in length. Approval does not mean that the boat is then Classified at Lloyd's or that it comes up to the full Lloyd's Rules for Yachts. Full Classification is rare with small boats. Other classification societies in other countries have similar schemes.

Maintenance and life

Like any other material GRP gradually deteriorates and its life depends on the degree of maintenance. It is immune to rot, insects and borers and, providing the gel coat is maintained intact, degradation of the laminate in water is extremely slow. Maintenance boils down to looking after the gel coat and if this is done the life of a GRP hull will be 20, 30, perhaps 50 years.

In the early years wax polishing is recommended. The underwater surfaces will need an anti-fouling paint because weed and barnacles adhere to GRP just as easily as to wood or steel. Wax polishing staves off the day when painting becomes necessary from an aesthetic point of view. The gel coat tends to fade after a few years (colours fading more quickly than white) just like a car body paint and the first step is to rub down with a car body rubbing compound or a metal polish such as Bluebell to bring back the shine. After a few times this process will not succeed as, especially in a coloured hull, the pigment in the gel coat may go blotchy. Then is the time for painting. This may come after five or seven years according to your own personal standards. There is no difficulty about painting GRP but the makers' recommendations on applying their paint to GRP must be followed. Several coats of polyurethane paint, applied in the best conditions, will last for another few years.

The inside surface of the hull needs no maintenance, especially if the boat is normally completely covered-in so that rainwater does not collect in the bilge. If the bilge is always wet it does pay to give the bilges a coat of paint to avoid the possibility of trouble through water absorption. Any accidental scrapes on the sides or bottom should not be left for too long before repairing. Deep scratches can be filled in with fresh gel coat from the boat builder to match the colour, while gashes or holes will need glass mat and resin, and perhaps a dummy 'mould' taped in place over the hole on the outside. A violent impact on a GRP hull causes local damage only—it does not strain the hull as a whole, as is the case with a timber hull. This is a particular advantage of GRP and greatly lessens the repair work.

If the gel coat resin is not flexible, fine cracks or crazing will appear after a few years, especially in areas which flex a great deal. This spoils the appearance and allows water to permeate into the interior of the laminate. Gel coats in which too large a quantity of colour pigment or filler have been incorporated are prone to water permeability. The water is trapped in voids between the gel coat and the laminate and causes blisters to appear sometimes after only a year or two, especially in fresh water. The osmotic pressure behind the gel coat is greater in fresh water than in salt. Too thin a gel coat will also cause this problem. Nowadays, the problems of blistering and crazing are well known and the resin manufacturers produce gel coat resins which, if applied properly, will avoid these troubles which were prevalent in early GRP boats.

A further advantage of GRP is that it does not leak. If a cockpit cover is fitted when the boat is not in use the bilge should remain dry. There is less chance of damp permeating the whole boat and in particular the engine will not rust so quickly. This advantage applies to any hull made in one piece— steel, aluminium or concrete. If the deck and superstructure are of GRP there will be no baffling drips from the deckhead as is likely in traditionally-built wooden boats. Fuel and water tanks can be moulded-in which puts to use otherwise useless space in the bilge, at the same time keeping the weight of these liquids low down in the boat.

GRP fuel tanks should be coated inside with a special resin since GRP is slightly attacked by fuels. Fresh water stored in GRP tanks sometimes has a bad taste. When this happens it is usually in a new boat and can be cured by repeated rinsing with hot water or vinegar, or by blowing in hot air for a few hours to complete the cure.

A disadvantage of GRP boats is that if they catch fire they burn very rapidly—more fiercely than a wooden boat. The resin burns leaving a hairy mass of glass fibres. There are such things as fire retardant resins, but these increase the cost of the moulding and reduce the strength. They also make the laminating business more difficult, because of their opacity. A layer of woven roving near the inner face of the laminate does tend to act as a fireguard. Another approach which is probably the most practical is to use intumescent paint in areas where the risk is greatest, around the engine and the galley. These paints present a barrier of incombustible foam and inert gas when a flame is applied.

GRP is not the cheapest way to make a hull. For one thing, the cost of the raw materials is high and likely to increase with the cost of oil. Although the advertised cost of a bare GRP hull seems cheap there is far greater work and cost in the out-fitting. A bare hull is really bare. To it has to be added timber strakes along the keel, bilge keels, gunwale, the engine bearers and frames or floors, before the hull can be said to be complete. A wooden or steel hull will already be this far complete.

GRP is not the lightest material. Table 4 (p. 116) gives a comparison between the different materials. The trouble with GRP is that it is relatively flexible. The thickness is dictated by the degree of flexibility that can be allowed, rather than a strength criterion, so hulls tend to be over-strong in order to be reasonably rigid. This can be overcome by having two GRP skins separated by a light core so that the overall thickness is much greater (thickness equals stiffness). Despite the weight of the core the overall construction is lighter. This is called sandwich construction and a hull can be made as light, or even lighter than, one of wood. The core can be expanded PVC foam, balsa wood, or paper and glass honeycombs. Additional advantages of a sandwich hull are effective heat insulation and corresponding freedom from condensation, and inherent buoyancy. But, as usual, there are snags. The bond between the core and the GRP skin must be capable of transmitting the loads without delaminating. The core itself now becomes the limiting factor which affects strength. It will be the first to crush or shear. The necessarily thin skins are more likely to puncture under impact. For these reasons whole hulls built in the sandwich scheme are usually larger than 30 ft. Balsa end-grain (Figure 38) makes the best core, but is expensive, and for hulls, PVC rigid foam is widely used. On smaller

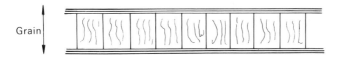

38   An end grain balsa GRP sandwich. It would not be so strong if the grain ran the other way

craft a sandwich construction is very good for cabin and wheelhouse roofs. Sufficient rigidity for walking on without the need for head-bruising beams, together with the elimination of condensation, are achieved at one stroke.

Rather than lay-up the resin and glass by hand it is attractive from the boat builders' point of view to spray a mix of resin and glass fibres directly onto the mould. One can imagine the difficulties on a vertical surface and how easy it would be to put on too much in one area and too little on another. The machines are expensive and have to be stripped and cleaned out after use. Quality control has to be even more strict. In fact not many boat builders use this method.

Wood

Wooden boats have been used for centuries and their longevity proved by craft afloat today that are 40, 50, 60 years' old and still in good condition. It is only by good maintenance that a wooden boat will last so long; neglected and disused, it will quickly succumb to rot and decay in a sad and pathetic way. Wooden construction has by no means died out, there are still builders in timber and, in fact, the price of a wooden boat is usually less than an equivalent one in GRP. This is particularly true on the second-hand market.

Whereas a GRP boat can be safely left afloat during the winter without a noticeable decline in its appearance inside or out, a wooden boat does not take kindly to this treatment. The bottom of a GRP hull still needs to be scrubbed and painted every year and the gel coat kept up to scratch, and ventilation made particularly free during the winter. A wooden boat needs warm and dry days ashore for repainting and re-varnishing, which will take several weekends of work. The autumn and winter are times when the whole boat becomes wet on the outside with dew and rain, with periods of days at a time when the water does not dry off during the daylight. Under these conditions any cracks or leaks will collect water which will get underneath varnish or paint to start the rot process. A sidedeck or gunwale can appear to be quite sound with an intact paint film, but the wood underneath can be completely rotten. It is stagnant rain water which creates conditions ripe for rot and the gunwale and sidedecks and the top of the transom are the most likely places for rot to start. The chances of rot starting are made small if the boat is covered with one large tarpaulin during the winter and through-ventilation arranged by leaving hatches and doors open. In warmer waters there are insects and borers to contend with. They are not unknown in European waters. However, there are anti-fouling paints which will keep them at bay. If proper maintenance is carried out the deterioration of the boat can be delayed so that when the boat is five years old it will still look new (more so than a GRP boat). A wooden hull left afloat continuously for several years on inland fresh waters, even if covered during the winter, will suffer greatly from deterioration, more so than one left on the sea. The frames and keel may well go soft depending on the species of timber.

All this may sound a depressing story, but there is no need to expect a wooden hull to fall apart after a few years—on the contrary, given reasonable maintenance it will last a lifetime. The modern glued timber construction tends to be more watertight and less liable to decay via pockets of trapped water and water in the bilge.

On the credit side timber construction has several advantages. Apart from rendering a boat cheaper on the second-hand market (from the buyer's point of view) it almost automatically gives the boat, particularly the inside of the cabin, a warm homely feel. Wood trim is added on a GRP boat to lose that clinical look, hide a rough moulding or to set off the smooth GRP finish. A wooden boat already has the wood trim.

Because timber falls into a naturally easy curve when bent, hulls built of planks or strips often have a grace and eye-catching sweep which only replicas of these shapes in GRP can attain. Clinker construction is particularly handsome in this way, not the double-ended lifeboat shape, but those with transom sterns and raked bows. Carvel hulls tend to have less flare at the bow because the planking is necessarily thicker and is more difficult to bend.

Other advantages of a wooden hull are that it does not 'sweat' inside so much; it absorbs engine vibration better than GRP or metal; it has no odour like a GRP hull and the more efficient forms give the lightest construction one can buy. For very fast boats this is a great advantage over GRP. For not-so-fast planing cruisers it is one of three materials possible—GRP, wood and aluminium (see Table 4). Apart from not having the condensation problem of steel, aluminium or GRP, thick wood is a good heat insulator and additional insulation is not needed.

There are several forms of timber construction, the common ones being sketched in Figure 39. For water tightness, clinker depends on the ability of wood to swell and seal any leaks. The seams are not caulked in any way. This is surprisingly effective and one would normally expect no more than half a bucketful of water to collect in the bilge in a week. At sea the joints work slightly and more water does come in. How much depends on how well the boat was built and its age. Clinker construction tends to prevent water climbing up the sides in a seaway (the plank lands forming multiple spray strakes) but, when stationary, even in the merest breeze, the lands of the planks

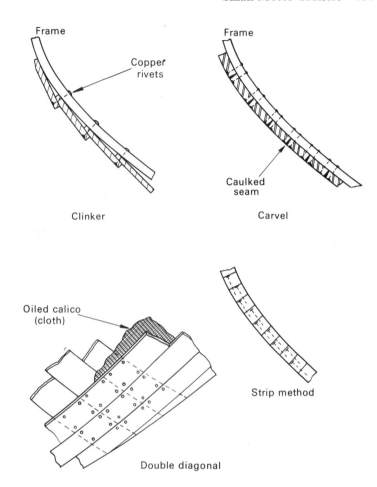

39 Timber construction

cause a continuous poppling noise—pleasant or otherwise depending on your temperament. With clinker there are no seams to maintain, but the protruding plank edges do make scraping and painting the underside that much more difficult.

In carvel construction the planks have to be made thicker in order to be successfully caulked. It is difficult to keep the seams intact in hot weather above the waterline or when the boat is out of the water. Like a clinker hull, after a period ashore, leakage can be quite dramatic for the first 24 hours or so.

Carvel construction is not normally to be found on fast boats because of the weight and the susceptibility of the seams when pounding in a choppy sea. To overcome these problems fast boats in the pre-GRP days were built of double-diagonal planking and this form is still occasionally used. It makes a light construction but the calico canvas which used to be placed between the skins is susceptible to rot and repair of such a hull is difficult.

A modern version of carvel planking is strip planking where each strip is glued and nailed to its neighbour, thus giving a watertight and very strong hull. It is not popular because it is time consuming to build. It can give more shape to a hull than carvel.

A plywood hull invariably means a hard-chine form and the flat panels need stiffening with frames or longitudinals. Marine grade plywood must be used, for instance BS 1088 marked with a WBP bond (water boil proof) and a British Standard Kitemark. It gives a very light and strong hull, completely watertight, but the problem of rot remains. Maintenance is probably less than with a carvel hull.

Probably the strongest and lightest form of construction of all is hot or cold moulded plywood. A male mould is used on which is stapled and glued together thin veneers (about $\frac{1}{8}$ in thick) of wood—like the basic manufacture of plywood but directly applied in the shape of a boat. Cold moulding refers to a glue which sets at room temperature, while hot moulding means that the whole mould and veneer assembly is put into a chamber and 'cooked'. These methods give a watertight hull with few frames or stiffeners to clutter the inside. It is relatively easy to maintain and paint. Being so strong and light it is a favourite method with fast boats—even race boats.

Of the various timber constructions, carvel and clinker are the most common. More people are familiar with timber as a material than with GRP, so there is less need to discuss how to inspect a wooden hull to see if it is well made. Evidence of poor workmanship cannot be hidden to the same extent as with GRP. On second-hand boats the places to inspect carefully for rot are the gunwales and sidedecks. Planked decks are notoriously difficult to keep watertight and there is the practice of laying the planks on plywood. Any leakage between the seams is trapped between the planks and the plywood and rot is almost certain to follow. Dirty, oily bilges are a sign of lack of maintenance and a smelly, fusty cabin with mould growing on cushions and bulkheads is a sign of poor ventilation and possible decay somewhere in the boat. A professional survey is well worth while before buying. Of course if a boat does have rot in places this does not condemn her—one advantage of timber construction is that it is easy to repair with simple tools.

Common timbers

Birch	Often used for plywood. Poor resistance to decay. 30–32 lb/cu ft.
Elm	English—strong but liable to warp; Canadian rock—the best elm for frames, stringers, keels. 35–50 lb/cu ft.
Gaboon	Light wood used for plywood. 25 lb/cu ft.
Iroko	Similar to teak but not quite so good. Used for deck planking.
Larch	Used for clinker planking. 37 lb/cu ft.
Mahogany	A cover-up name nowadays for such African hardwoods as sapele. Honduras mahogany is best with good resistance to decay and gives a good finish for varnishing. African mahogany is moderately resistant and is slightly pink in colour. About 35 lb/cu ft.
Oak	English oak makes the best sawn-timbers, knees, stem, keel etc. Must be well seasoned.
Pine	Oregan and Columbian pine (Douglas fir) make good masts, but are susceptible to rot. 33 lb/cu ft.
Pitch pine	Very resistant to decay, but the term often includes inferior species such as loblolly pine. 46 lb/cu ft.
Spruce	Light wood used for spars. Not very durable. 28 lb/cu ft.
Teak	Probably the best wood. Very resistant to decay. About the only wood that can be left unpainted without harm. 40–45 lb/cu ft.

Note: The quality of a certain species of timber can vary enormously. It depends on the actual location and quality of the tree, how the timber was seasoned and how it was selected. There are effective wood preservers available nowadays so there is no excuse for the wood boat builder not to treat all his timber—or at least those parts which are liable to decay.

Steel

Steel has a character of its own. Its advantages are that it is enormously strong, does not leak, is immune to borers, is a cheap material, and gives a boat inherent ballast and an easy motion at sea. Welding has superseded rivetting, but this process causes considerable distortion to thin plating and a great deal of skill is needed to weld the hull in a sequence designed to minimise distortion and then subsequently to heat and hammer flat the worst affected areas. Chine hulls with the surfaces having curvature only in one direction are naturally easier to make. As there is no chance of making a steel planing boat the hard-chine hull form need not follow planing boat style. The chine can be kept low, even below the water, and some handsome shapes can be found even with a single chine (Figure 40). A double chine hull is a step towards the round-bilge form which is itself possible. The Dutch are well known

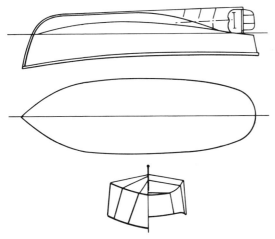

40   Single chine tug-shaped steel hull

for their round-bilge steel hulls, so well faired it is difficult to tell at first glance whether the hull is of steel or wood.

The minimum thickness of plate is limited by the distortion due to welding, and by corrosion, to about $\frac{1}{8}$ in. As a displacement boat is inherent in the choice of steel, weight is a positive advantage and $\frac{3}{16}$ in thickness is a better proposition. From Table 4 it will be obvious that steel plate needs to be supported by stiffeners (Figure 41) at fairly close spacing to avoid accidental denting, although curvature will greatly increase the

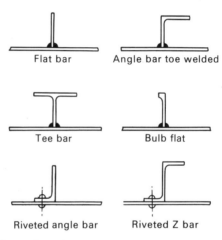

Flat bar   Angle bar toe welded

Tee bar   Bulb flat

Riveted angle bar   Riveted Z bar

41   Stiffeners for steel or aluminium hulls

resistance to denting. On the other hand, steel has an enormous reserve of strength and the chance of tearing the plating by hitting an underwater obstruction is slight. In this sense steel makes a very safe boat. The steel used can deform and yield like rubber to a considerable extent. It is not a high strength steel, as steels go, but is ductile, not easily cracking, and is called mild steel. Steel is, of course, fireproof. It is the densest material used for hulls and if the boat does happen to fill with water it will sink like a stone.

The main problem with steel is rust. Modern paint schemes produced by the large paint manufacturers as used on ships have gone a long way to beating the rust problem. Although paint is the usual protection, galvanising or zinc spraying is sometimes employed. Galvanising is perhaps the best answer but, even so, the whole hull cannot be dipped and the welded seams will still need painting or zinc spraying. Zinc spraying is not so good as galvanising—the zinc coating does not adhere to the steel as well as zinc deposited by hot galvanising. It is usually the welded seams that rust first and produce streaks of rust running down the hull sides.

The modern exotic paints—polyurethane, epoxy and chlorinated rubbers, for instance—must be applied to the bare steel in a dry, warm atmosphere to prevent rust successfully for several years. Shot blasting is the best method to obtain a good surface. Wire brushing is not nearly so effective. For DIY work a disc sander using a tungsten carbide grit disc is best. With these facts in mind one can gain an idea of how well the boat builder does the job of protecting his hulls. After that it is up to regular repainting to keep rust at bay.

Other disadvantages of steel are that without insulation the inside of the boat will sweat badly and, because of the lack of inherent damping and the hard surface of steel, engine noise will be that much greater. Both these problems can be overcome by the use of close-fitting or glued-on insulation (foam-backed vinyl, for instance) and good engine insulation, particularly by flexibly mounting the engine. Because steel is more popular for inland-water boats the material is described further in Chapter 11.

Aluminium

Many of the remarks on steel as a hull material relate to aluminium. The advantages of aluminium are that it does not rust and it makes a considerably lighter hull—in fact, in thin-plate rivetted form (aircraft-type structure) it vies with hot-moulded plywood construction as the lightest material. Pure aluminium is soft and weak and to be structurally useful has to be alloyed with a small quantity of, for example, copper or magnesium. Copper based aluminium alloys are most unsuitable for marine use—they corrode away after a time in sea water. The correct type of aluminium alloy must be used and

Table 3. The electrochemical series

Stainless steel
Copper
Phosphor bronze
Brass
Gunmetal
Aluminium bronze
Monel (cast)
Manganese bronze
Cast iron
Lead
Mild steel
Cadmium plated steel
Aluminium
Galvanised mild steel
Zinc
Magnesium

(i) If two different metals are in contact with one another the further apart they are in the series the more vigorous the electrolytic action.

(ii) The metal lower in the series will be attacked. The higher one (the more 'noble' of the two) will be protected.

(iii) To minimise the electrolytic action the two metals should be close together in the series and the one with the larger area should be the anode (i.e. the lower in the series), Figure 42.

(iv) Stainless steel should not be used underwater except where its whole area will be open to water flow, e.g. propeller shafts.

Fastenings

Fitting metal	*Fastener*
Galvanised	Use galvanised or manganese bronze. Avoid brass
Aluminium	Use aluminium, cadmium-plated, galvanised or stainless steel. Avoid copper or brass
Stainless steel	Use stainless steel. Avoid galvanised or steel
Copper	Use copper. Avoid galvanised or steel
Steel	Use steel, stainless steel or manganese bronze. Avoid brass or copper
Steel hulls	(i) Blocks of zinc or magnesium are often fitted below the waterline to act as a sacrificial anode.
	(ii) Fasteners should be steel or slightly above mild steel in the series.
	(iii) Aluminium should be insulated electrically.
	(iv) Manganese bronze or Monel shafts are best.

Aluminium
hulls
(i) Fasteners should be aluminium or above aluminium in the series, e.g. cadmium-plated or stainless steel.

(ii) Manganese bronze or stainless steel shafts are best, but they should be electrically insulated from the hull.

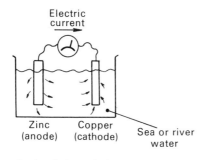

Basis of electrolysis

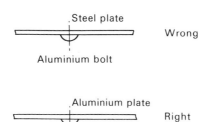

those developed for marine use usually contain 3 to 5 per cent of magnesium.

Aluminium alloys are divided into heat-treatable and non-heat-treatable types. The heat-treatable types (usually magnesium and silicon alloys) are considerably stronger, but welding reduces the strength around the weld back to the unheat-treated state. Thus to utilise the extra strength the hull has to be rivetted. The other type of alloy—the non-heat-treatable—can be strengthened during manufacture by work-hardening ($\frac{1}{4}$ hard, $\frac{1}{2}$ hard etc.) but this process is also destroyed by welding.

The choice therefore lies between a rivetted hull of a strong heat-treatable alloy, or a welded hull made of thicker non-heat-treatable alloy. As with steel, there is a practical minimum for welding of about $\frac{1}{8}$ in, but even with this thicker plate the weight of the complete hull is low (see Table 4). There is no particular problem in welding aluminium and it produces a strong watertight hull.

The types of alloy suitable for marine work are covered by various standards, for instance, British Standard 1470 (plate, sheet and strip) and 1476 (bars, extruded tube and sections). In their nomenclature N stands for non-heat-treatable, H for heat-treatable, E for bars and sections and S for plate or sheet. Thus the marine grades of aluminium are N5, N6, N8, H30 and H20; a plate would be called up as HS30 for example, and a T-bar as NE8. These alloys have given very good service in, for example, lifeboats over a great many years.

Marine grade aluminium is extremely resistant to deterioration even if not painted. However, if you own an aluminium boat electrolytic problems have to be guarded against—never tie-up for a long period to a steel boat! Any fittings of a different metal should be electrically insulated and the metal should be higher in the electrochemical series, e.g. stainless steel (see Table 3).

Mercury or copper-based anti-fouling paints should never be used on an aluminium hull. These metals are far too high up in the series relative to aluminium.

Although aluminium is used for larger craft, for instance large motor yachts and patrol boats, it is uncommon among small cruisers, probably because of the high cost of the raw material. Nevertheless, it has great merits and only a few problems, easily overcome.

Concrete

This unlikely-sounding hull material has a number of great advantages. More properly it is called ferro-cement as it is formed from steel reinforcement, in the form of wire mesh, and a special cement. A framework of steel rods and many layers of wire mesh is set up in the shape of the hull. A team of plasterers then come along and slap on the cement, pressing it through the mesh and smoothing the outside like the interior walls of a house. When cured, the hull is sanded down and painted. There is a practical limit to how thin the hull can be made (about $\frac{1}{2}$ in) and most hulls are about $\frac{3}{4}$–1 in thick. The material is heavy (see Table 4) and the hull turns out to be about as heavy as one of steel. For displacement boats this is of no great consequence, but ferro-cement planing boats are not feasible at present. Concrete boats can be classed at Lloyd's who also approve some makes of cement and mesh.

The advantages of a hull made in concrete are (a) it is a one-piece hull and therefore watertight; (b) it does not rot or corrode; (c) it is extremely fire resistant; (d) it is extremely strong under impact loads—a collision for instance. One would imagine the material to be brittle and crack easily, but, in fact, it is quite resilient and will bend and yield to some extent like steel or aluminium. It is fairly good from the condensation point of view, and it has no odour like GRP.

Its disadvantage is that like GRP it has a low abrasion resistance so rubbing strips are required in areas where abrasion is likely. The surface chips easily, but on the other hand it is easily filled (in most climatic conditions, unlike GRP) and smoothed off again. Although painting is not necessary to protect the concrete it is needed for appearance. The surface finish is not very good compared to GRP. Antifouling is still necessary. In poorly built hulls, where perhaps the wrong materials were used, the steelwork rusts and the rust appears on the outside. Properly built, using for example Lloyd's approved materials, concrete makes an excellent hull and by all accounts a cheap one.

The strains experienced by a boat hull in a rough sea are of far less importance than those experienced when the boat is lifted out of the water and placed on two keel blocks, or when the boat dries out on hard ground, or is jostled and thumped against a jetty. Damage to a hull usually occurs through

Table 4. Weights and strengths of different hull materials

	Specific gravity of material (water = 1)	Typical thickness of a 24 ft hull in	Typical weight of a 24 ft bare hull lb	Load to break a horizontal strip 1 ft wide 4 ft long supported at ends lb	Deflection of same strip with load of 50 lb in	Comments
GRP (CSM)	1·5	$\frac{5}{16}$/($\frac{1}{4}$ sides)	860	187 (sides)	5·3	Flexible but strong
GRP sandwich	—	$\frac{3}{4}$ ($\frac{1}{2}$ core, $\frac{1}{8}$ skins)	760	400–500 (depends on core material)	0·25	Efficient structure but difficult to repair
Carvel (mahog)	0·58	$\frac{3}{4}$	1030	1030	0·19	Heavy but strong
Clinker (mahog)	0·58	$\frac{1}{2}$	790	535	0·28	Lighter but still strong
Plywood	0·59	$\frac{1}{2}$	610	250	0·64	Light and strong, no leaks
Strip (mahog)	0·58	$\frac{3}{4}$	830	1030	0·19	Light and strong, no leaks
Cold/hot moulded plywood	0·59	$\frac{1}{2}$	560	250	0·64	Very light and strong, no leaks
double diagonal	0·6	$\frac{1}{2}$	750	a cut-out strip would be very weak		Canvas rots, difficult to repair
Steel	7·8	$\frac{3}{16}$	3000	200 to dent	0·57	Very heavy but very strong
Aluminium	2.65	$\frac{1}{8}$	730	46 to dent	5·9	Light and strong, no rust
Concrete	2·4	$\frac{5}{8}$	2750	350	0.36	Heavy but strong; no leaks or corrosion

grounding or collision; it is unlikely to be damaged purely by wave force except in the case of fast boats. The pounding forces on the bottom are the greatest the hull of a fast boat is likely to experience, and this area needs to be extremely strong and well stiffened.

The thickness and frame sizes of a small boat are therefore chosen with these needs in mind—robustness to take knocks and to take the ground. Columns 5 and 6 in Table 4 give a comparative idea of the strength and flexibility of the different materials to impact loads. It is only a very rough guide because the extent of internal framing will make a great difference. For instance, steel and aluminium will dent fairly easily, but actually to rupture and tear the plate takes an enormous load. The materials yield and stretch to a much greater extent than wood or GRP. A GRP sandwich is rather prone to impact damage because of the necessarily thin skins. The core will only help back-up the outer skin to a certain extent. Balsa cores are better than foam cores from this point of view. On the other hand notice the much greater stiffness of the sandwich to a single skin GRP panel. Also notice how flexible GRP is, compared to all the other materials except aluminium. Timber could form a study all of its own. It is a complicated material compared with steel or even GRP. For one thing, the strength and flexibility of different species of timber varies enormously, and so do the properties within a single tree. It is also complicated by the fact that wood has much greater strength in one direction than another, unlike steel or CSM GRP. Plywood or moulded construction partially overcomes these problems. Generally a wood hull is light, stiff and strong. Structurally timber is a very good material.

6 Engines and their Installation

Reliability

The engine of a motor cruiser is its source of propulsion. A breakdown while cruising on a canal or river is merely embarrassing (except near a weir) but at sea it can be fatal. For a sea-going cruiser the reliability of the engine is the most important factor of all. Reliability boils down essentially to maintenance, but even the most inherently reliable and well maintained engine may fail at some time or other.

To be on the safe side an alternative means of propulsion is desirable. A twin screw and engine arrangement, with separate fuel and electrical systems, is the ideal solution. Alternatively, a mast on which a sail can be spread with its centre of effort occurring roughly amidships, will give propulsion downwind or beam on. The simplest makeshift most commonly used is a small outboard, normally stowed away, but ready to ship on a bracket on the transom. The size of outboard required becomes rather cumbersome on boats over about 25 ft in length, especially if it is intended to provide propulsion in choppy conditions. An outboard of about 5 h.p. is sufficient for boats up to about 20 ft but at least 10 h.p. is required for a 25 footer. Even then progress into a strong wind and choppy sea will be very slow.

If the engine breaks down at sea the boat will probably drift sideways-on to the wind and waves. This is a most uncomfortable and dangerous attitude and makes repair work on the engine or the shipping of the emergency outboard difficult. The motion will be eased a little if the anchor and some chain is let out and allowed to drag through the water, or a sea-anchor streamed out. If she drifts into shallow water the anchor will start to bite and prevent her going ashore. The most essential piece of equipment on a single screw sea-going motor boat is the anchor and chain.

The owner who does his own maintenance will be more familiar with the engine and thus more likely to be able to tackle a repair job at sea. Even simple jobs need a screwdriver, a pair of pliers and a few spanners, so a tool kit is a necessary part of the engine installation, and of course the engine hand-book should be carried on board. A spare can or tank of fuel stowed aboard will overcome the possibility of running out of fuel (the fuel gauge may stick without it being realised).

The engine of a motor cruiser should be unobtrusive both in terms of the space it takes up and the noise and vibration it causes. Those who take up boating to escape the noise and bustle of the roads and choose a motor cruiser fitted with a large diesel may find that they have brought the noise along with them. On a small boat it is inescapable.

First cost and economy in running are other aspects. Economy is dealt with in Chapter 8. Although reliability is the first priority of safety at sea, safety of operation depends on the fuel and how the fuel system is installed. There have been many explosions and fires caused by a fuel spillage while refuelling, or by a petrol leak filling the bilges with petrol vapour to be ignited by a cigarette or a pilot light on a gas refrigerator. Unlike a motor car, fuel or gas leaks cannot drop harmlessly away but collect in the bilges.

The questions this chapter aims to answer are, what are the pros and cons of the different engines and different drives? and, how to tell if the engine is installed safely and to a good standard. The choice of engine basically lies between an in-board (diesel or petrol), and an outboard.

Inboard engines

The term 'inboard' refers to an engine mounted inside the hull driving a propeller shaft passing through a watertight gland in the bottom of the hull. The engine must be fitted in the middle of the boat and takes up room in the cabin or cockpit. The gland in the stern tube must be greased fre-quently and repacked every few years to prevent more than the odd few drops of water dripping into the bilge. The line of the propeller shaft must be sloped to allow the propeller room to swing underneath the hull. This reduces propeller efficiency slightly especially if the angle of the shaft to the horizontal is more than 10°. Unless protected by a keel the propeller is prone to damage, particularly if the boat runs aground, and how difficult clearing ropes and polythene bags from the propeller is depends on how far forward from the transom, and how deeply, it is situated. On boats smaller than about 25 ft it is usually just possible to reach the propeller from a dinghy.

An engine situated *in* the boat rather than hung on the transom can be kept dry and protected, which has a bearing on reliability. However, if the cockpit is left uncovered and the engine box allows rainwater to trickle onto the engine this advantage is lost and the engine quickly corrodes. The life of an engine in a boat is often said to be determined by rusting rather than running hours. This is certainly true if water is allowed to run over the engine or condensation to collect because the box is not ventilated. Corrosion will be accelerated if bilge water collects under the engine. Completely watertight hulls such as those made of GRP avoid this defect and the engine in such a boat stands a greater chance of coming to the end of its life through sheer running hours. The average running time of a pleasure boat in a season is only about 100 to 150 hours. This running time in a car would represent 3000–4500 miles assuming an average speed of 30 m.p.h. Thus an automotive engine in a boat will last, in terms of wearing out, for at least 20 years! Diesels will last even longer.

Diesel or petrol

With an inboard installation the choice lies mainly between diesel and petrol. Arguments about their relative merits are frequently heard or read. At the moment there is little competition from other types, such as the steam engine, the Stirling, the Wankel, the battery-electric motor or the gas turbine. In principle petrol engines are lighter, less bulky, cheaper in first cost and readily maintained and repaired by anyone with a knowledge of cars, but they use a hazardous and expensive fuel and the electrics, in particular, are liable to fail from the presence of water. In comparison, diesels are heavy, bulky and costly. They also give greater vibration and noise and the fuel is smelly and soaks into woodwork to give off a permeating smell. On the other hand they are basically more reliable and use a much cheaper and safer fuel.

The true marine engine built only for marine work is becoming uncommon. These engines are slow running, directly cooled by seawater or river water pumped through the cylinder jackets and are bulky and heavy whether petrol or diesel. Today most diesel and petrol engines fitted in boats are of automotive or industrial origin, i.e. the basic engine is fitted in cars and trucks, or used as the prime mover in air compressors, agricultural machinery, generating sets etc. The adaptation for marine use consists of fitting a marine gearbox, a seawater pump and in most cases a heat exchanger, so that only fresh water is circulated through the cylinder jackets. Also any parts that might corrode badly in a salt environment are replaced or treated. The advantages of such engines are lightness (they are high revving engines) and compactness and, since they are made in their thousands, comparatively low price. Spares are readily available and the basic engines are well-proven and have a long life.

To illustrate the differences between the various types of engine two Ford units will be examined. Ford produce engines mainly for cars (petrol) and trucks (diesel) but a large number of firms marinise the basic units. For instance their 2264 engine is a 4-cylinder 1600 cc petrol unit. Marinised it produces a maximum of 60 h.p. at 4500 r.p.m. A corresponding 4-cylinder diesel of about the same horsepower—the Ford 2401E—produces 58 h.p. at 3600 r.p.m. but has a capacity of 2360 cc.

Diesel and petrol engines are basically very similar, the same configuration of crankshaft, piston, cylinder and valves being used. The differences lie in the methods of metering and firing the mixture of fuel and air. In the petrol engine a carburettor mixes petrol and air in the correct ratio and the mixture is then exploded inside the cylinder by a spark. In the diesel the air enters the cylinder and is compressed, and hence heated to such an extent that when fuel is injected into the cylinder spontaneous combustion takes place. A fuel injection pump is thus necessary on a diesel and this precision-made item is the weak point of the diesel. It also limits the r.p.m. at which a diesel can run, so that a diesel has to be of a greater capacity than a petrol engine to achieve the same horse power. Also the running gear-pistons, crankshaft etc. have to be much stronger to withstand the higher cylinder pressures.

Thus it is that the Ford diesel is heavier and bulkier than the petrol engine. The marinised 1600 cc Ford petrol engine weighs about 325 lb and has dimensions of about 36 × 21 × 23 in (length × breadth × height). The 58 h.p. diesel weighs about 665 lb and has dimensions of about 41 × 28 × 27 in. Partly because the diesel is a physically bigger engine and partly because it is made to higher engineering standards it costs more—£1150 as against about £525. Both engines have electric start and charging. Because the diesel is heavier to turn over (it has a compression ratio of around 20:1) it requires a more powerful starter motor and a larger and more costly battery (120 amp hour compared with 40 amp hour).

Petrol engines are usually cooled by pumping sea or river water straight through the block (Figure 43) whereas diesels

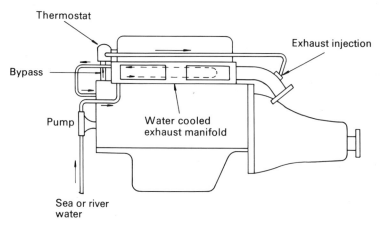

43   *Direct raw water cooling*

are more often cooled by heat exchanger (Figure 44). That is
to say fresh water is pumped through the block (as in a car or
truck) and the heat it collects is exchanged to the sea or river
water, inside the heat exchanger. With direct sea-water cooling
the temperature must be kept below about 57°C (135°F),

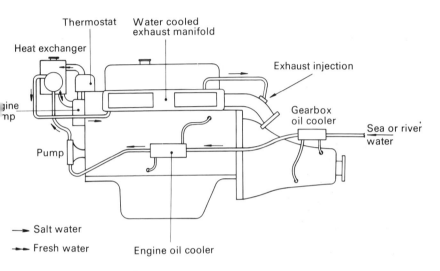

44   Heat exchanger cooling

otherwise salt tends to solidify inside the engine. This is a
much lower temperature than was intended by the engine
designers and the engines tend to wear out more quickly and
the combustion process is not so clean or efficient. Heat
exchanger cooling allows a temperature approaching boiling
to be maintained as in a car or truck. The diesel is more
susceptible to troubles resulting from cool running. The
injector nozzles are subject to cold corrosion by acids formed
during combustion.

Keel cooling is sometimes employed. In this system a bank
of pipes is arranged underneath the hull, alongside the keel,
through which the hot water from the engine is passed. The
temperature can be maintained higher than in a direct-cooled
system. Whichever cooling system is used a positive-displace-

ment pump has to be fitted to the engine to circulate the cooling water and this, unlike the water pump of a car engine, requires regular attention.

The extra weight of a diesel is of no consequence in a displacement boat but is a severe handicap to small planing boats. This is why there are few diesel-engined planing cruisers under 25 feet. Above this length the extra weight diminishes in importance relative to the all-up weight of the boat.

Although a diesel costs more initially, its fuel costs are much lower. In the UK diesel fuel bought at the waterside is exempt from the tax placed on fuel for road vehicles and consequently costs much less than petrol.

A diesel uses fuel more efficiently so that it consumes about 20–25 per cent less per horsepower produced. Assuming that under normal cruising conditions the two Ford engines produce 30 h.p., the consumption would be about 2 gallons an hour for the petrol engine and about $1\frac{1}{2}$ gallons an hour for the diesel. Let us take diesel fuel as costing 50p per gallon and petrol £1. The difference in running cost per hour is thus £1·25. In a season of 100 hours running the diesel would therefore save £125. At this rate it would be nine years before the fuel economy of the diesel offset its extra initial cost. This argument is rather hypothetical, but it does show that it takes a long time for the economy of the diesel to pay dividends.

A diesel is usually much noisier than a petrol engine. This is inherent because of the higher compression ratio and the higher peak pressures reached inside the cylinder. Noise does depend a great deal on how the engine is installed and the size of the boat. In a 20 ft boat it is difficult to escape from the noise of a centrally-mounted engine. In a 30-footer one is likely to be physically further away.

Whether an engine will be noisy or not depends on three things—whether it is diesel or petrol, whether it is flexibly mounted, and how well the engine box is insulated. Four-cylinder high speed automotive engines are flexibly mounted with success in cars and the same degree of isolation can be achieved in a boat. Rubber mounts cut the noise path between engine and hull. In a rigidly mounted installation the whole hull, and particularly panels which are not very stiff, will vibrate in sympathy with the engine, sending out their own noise waves and adding to the noise actually coming from the engine, rather like a sounding box. Flexible mounts serve both to reduce vibration *and* noise. However an automotive petrol engine can often be rigidly mounted in a boat without giving rise to excessive noise and vibration; it depends on the mass and rigidity of the engine bearers and the hull. But flexible mounts can make a petrol-engined boat as quiet and smooth as a good car.

The automotive diesel often causes the most excruciating amount of noise and vibration. The worst cases occur in hulls built from unstiffened panels of a resilient material such as GRP, steel or aluminium and where the engine is large for the size of hull, for instance, an 80 h.p. engine in a 25 ft boat. Rigidly mounted to undersized engine bearers, the engine will cause the whole boat to shake, especially at lower revs, and the noise will be such that conversation is impossible at anything above idling. In such boats one wonders whether the bottom is going to fall out.

Sometimes flexible mounts appear to make matters worse or at least no better, and the cause is usually that the engine bearers are moving in sympathy with the engine, in other words they are not stiff enough. To work effectively rubber mounts need to be bolted down to a massive (in comparison with the engine) and rigid surface. Engine bearers, apart from being massive, should end on a bulkhead or deep floor or on the transom. There should also be transverse frames attached to the bearers in order to hold them rigidly upright. Flexible mounts are essential to keep the noise level of a diesel down to acceptable levels. If the engine is rigidly mounted no amount of insulation around the engine will be very effective. Marine-type rubber mounts have in-built stops to prevent too much movement in a seaway. All pipes and controls connecting to the engine must be flexible to accommodate small movements.

Diesel fuel, unlike petrol, does not vaporise at ordinary temperatures so there is little danger that fumes may build up in the bilges, possibly leading to an explosion. Similarly diesel fuel catches light less readily so it constitutes a much safer fuel. Of course once alight it burns very well.

Maintenance

A diesel can also be said to be safer because it is less liable to breakdown. It needs regular attention like a petrol engine but not so often. Both engines will require oil and oil filter changes probably once a season. The petrol engine will require new contact breakers perhaps every two seasons and new sparking plugs perhaps every three seasons. Petrol filters and carburettor jets should be cleaned at least every season. There will also be the water intake filter to clean and the stern tube greaser to be turned once a week. Seawater pumps usually have a flexible neoprene impeller which lasts only a few years. During the winter the engine should be drained of water, unless antifreeze is added in the case of a closed-circuit system (heat exchanger), and the face plate of the pump should be slackened off to drain any water trapped there. The engine should be preserved for the winter as recommended in the manufacturers' handbook. This is usually done by running on a mixture of fuel and preserving oil for a few minutes in the case of a diesel, or dripping preserving oil into the carburettor intake while the engine is running in the case of a petrol engine. The fuel tanks should preferably be left full to minimise condensation accumulating inside. The battery should be taken home and charged monthly through the winter.

The two main causes of petrol engine failure are ignition trouble and dirt in the fuel. Dirt and water (mainly from condensation) collect in fuel tanks in boats to a greater extent than in cars. Ignition failure is usually due to pitted or dirty contact breakers or moisture shorting the circuit. Regular maintenance and cleaning as outlined above much reduce the chances of a breakdown.

The diesel must be fed with absolutely clean fuel and this is achieved by a single or duplex paper fuel filter usually fitted on the engine. The regular renewal of the filter element (every season) is vital. If this is done, trouble with the fuel pump and injectors should be of very rare occurrence. The injection pump must never be tampered with. Servicing must be done professionally. Air in the fuel lines causes most diesels to stop. If the lines are tight and the tank is never allowed to run dry and the fuel cock at the tank normally left 'on', air should never enter the system. Bleeding a diesel to rid the fuel system of air is fairly simple with the aid of a few spanners, but it has to be done in a certain sequence—hence the need to keep the engine handbook on board. Diesels are renowned for reliability and this is probably mostly due to the lack of an electrical ignition system.

Automotive diesels cannot be started by hand because of the high compression ratio and because truck engines are not fitted with decompression devices. So knowledge of the state of charge of the battery is an important factor.

Although this discussion of the relative merits of diesels and petrol engines has revolved around two Ford engines it could just as well have been based on engines, for example, from Perkins, BLMC, Volvo (their larger engines), Renault or Mercedes.

True marine engines

The distinguishing mark which separates true marine engines from the automotive variety is the r.p.m. at which they run. Installed in a boat a slow-speed true marine engine appears to give effortless speed on opening the throttle a little. The response is immediate and the boat seems to cover a lot of ground per revolution of the engine. But there seems to be little power left when opening the throttle wide. The range of revs is much less; typically, they idle at 600 r.p.m. with a maximum of 1800 r.p.m. This means that, even idling, the boat will travel at a fair speed. On the other hand a high speed automotive engine in a boat gives the impression of running fast for little result in terms of boat speed. It is not until 2000–3000 r.p.m. is reached before the boat seems to go. Naturally more noise comes from a high speed engine but, on the other hand, less vibration. A high speed diesel can be so noisy that one feels physically sick. The noise level is made worse if the engine is situated in a wheelhouse where the noise bounces back off the roof.

Two true marine engines will now be examined, the Stuart

Turner 10 h.p. two-stroke petrol engine and the Sabb 10 h.p. diesel. The Stuart Turner is a 2-cylinder two-stroke running on a petrol/oil mixture, weighs 258 lb and costs almost £300. The Sabb is a single cylinder engine weighing 440 lb and costs about £525. Again the disparity between petrol and diesel is clear. What is noticeable is that these engines weigh almost as much as the Ford engines of much greater horsepower. The Stuart Turner engine has a maximum r.p.m. of 1650 and the Sabb of 1800. Whereas direct drive is adequate for these engines, automotive engines usually require a reduction ratio of at least 2:1. Both the Sabb and the Stuart Turner are bolted rigidly down to the hull. It is difficult to mount flexibly single or twin-cylinder slow-running engines so as to reduce vibration transmitted to the boat. The Sabb diesel has the reputation of giving a not-unpleasant 'thump-thump' noise. Petrol engines of the true marine variety often have magneto ignition rather than a coil. There is still a contact breaker inside the magneto (which needs to be replaced regularly), but the magneto is usually a drip-proof item. On the other hand magnetos tend to age and begin to fail intermittently when hot in a most irritating manner. My own opinion is that magnetos are best avoided or converted by adding a car-type coil, still utilising the distributor part of the magneto. Thus the high tension current is produced by the battery and coil rather than the suspect magneto windings. The advantage of a magneto is that it makes the engine independent of a battery. Again these remarks about Sabb and Stuart Turner engines could equally well be applied to such makes as Brit, Wickstrom, Kelvin and Gardner.

A similar type of engine results from the marinisation of industrial engines—such as Lister. For example their 13 h.p. (at 2000 r.p.m.) SR2M engine is an air-cooled twin-cylinder diesel built to last a lifetime with a great reputation for reliability. For comparison, the weight is 600 lb and it costs about £400. With solid mounts and air cooling it is a very noisy engine but the air cooling has its advantages. There is nothing to go wrong with the cooling system (it has a flywheel fan blowing air over finned cylinders). There is no water inlet and filter or water pump. The hot air can sometimes be usefully used for warming the cabin or the helmsman's feet. Other examples of engines of industrial origin are the Petter, Enfield and Farymann.

Paraffin

Some petrol engines, notably those which are designed to run slowly and have a low compression ratio, can be converted to run on paraffin, the attraction being the low cost of the fuel (approximately the price of diesel fuel). The engine is started on petrol and when warm is switched over to paraffin. This entails a dual-fuel system with two tanks. Paraffin is a relatively 'dirty' fuel and the engine will require de-coking much more frequently; it is also a smelly fuel. It reduces the power of the engine and when idling for long periods vaporisation may cease causing the engine to stall. Wickstrom and Volvo produce paraffin engines.

Gearboxes

There is often a choice between a manual gearbox and one which is hydraulically operated. (There is also a choice of reduction ratios which is discussed fully in Chapter 7.) Manual gearbox refers to manual engagement of ahead and astern. A long gear lever on the side of the gearbox works a cam which tightens the appropriate brake band causing engagement of ahead or astern. This lever must exert enough force to tighten the brake bands sufficiently so that they do not slip. Any slip at full throttle will quickly burn the bands. Adjustment of these brake bands has to be done carefully and regularly (perhaps once every two seasons). The reverse mechanism itself is usually lubricated by grease nipples and only if a reduction gear (in a separate box bolted to the aft end of the gearbox) is fitted will there be an oil bath.

In a hydraulically-operated box the brake bands or clutches are moved by small hydraulic rams, oil under pressure being supplied by a small pump inside the gearbox. The force the rams produce is comparatively large so that no slipping can take place and the brake bands need no regular adjustment. A valve mechanism feeds oil to the required ram. Very little effort is required to operate the valve lever so remote control is easily achieved with push-pull cable. Single lever remote control can then be achieved, i.e. moving the lever forwards first engages ahead and then applies throttle, and similarly moving the lever backwards gives astern; throttle and gear shift are combined. This naturally makes control of the boat easier rather than having a separate gear lever, possibly just aft of the engine box, and a throttle fitted on the bulkhead by the wheel. Hydraulically-operated boxes are more expensive and also are less efficient in that a little power is lost. The box is partially filled with oil, which will require changing periodically, together with an oil filter. The power lost reappears as heat in the oil and so a small heat exchanger is usually fitted through which cold seawater is passed on its way to the engine.

Installation

One can sum up the requirements for a good engine installation in this way: it should be reliable, economical, unobtrusive in size and noise yet easily accessible, and the installation should be safe. To achieve this ideal the details of installation are just as important as the choice of engine. Flexible mounts are necessary to achieve real quietness irrespective of engine make and the fuel feed system must be properly fitted for reliability and safety.

In a petrol installation a pump feed to the carburettor, with the tank fitted low down in the hull, is much safer than a gravity feed. There are two reasons for this. First, after switching off the engine, the needle valve in the carburettor can sometimes be held slightly off its seating by a piece of dirt. In the case of gravity feed this will mean that petrol will drip continuously into the bilge. Secondly, in a similar way petrol will be fed to a fire if the fire causes the pipe to leak.

Many installations do, in fact, have gravity feed and it is essential that (a) the petrol pipe is copper or steel and the

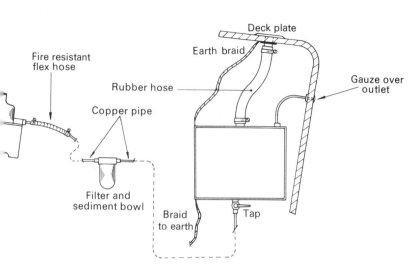

45   *Important features of a petrol feed installation*

flexible portion adjoining the carburettor is armoured and fire resistant (b) there is a tap at the petrol tank which is easily accessible and (c) you turn the petrol tap off each time the engine is stopped (Figure 45).

In the case of a pump feed, a tap at the tank is not really necessary, but the petrol pipe should still be fire resistant (certainly not plastic pipe). In the event of an engine fire, switching off the engine will at least stop any further petrol reaching the flames.

There should be a water trap and a fine mesh filter near the petrol tank and again this should be readily accessible. Glass-bowled traps make it easy to see how much dirt has collected but a copper bowl is safer in the event of a fire. Ideally a petrol tank should not be of copper or galvanised steel because a gum or sediment is sometimes produced over a long period of time. Bare steel will rust on the inside which will not help matters. The deck filler, tank and engine should be electrically linked and earthed with wire braid. This lessens the chance of a spark occurring between the deck filler and the nozzle of the petrol bowser when refuelling.

In a diesel installation leakage is more of a nuisance than a danger. A tap at the tank need only be used when disconnecting the fuel pipe for any reason. To forget to open it before starting the engine will probably lead to air getting into the system, so it is usually better to leave it open. Copper and galvanised steel tanks sometimes give rise to the same problems with diesel fuel as with petrol over a long period so again these materials are best avoided. With a diesel installation there should be a large water and sediment filter bowl fitted in the fuel line just before the fuel lift pump on the engine. When the boat rolls this will catch the worst of the sediment and water stirred up in the tanks.

Stainless steel is probably the best tank material for any fuel. In GRP tanks, self-quenching resins to BS 476 should be used; the trouble is, one never knows. Also, in the case of a built-in tank the bond to the hull is susceptible to leaks particularly if the boat works in this area. Bonded properly, a GRP tank is quite satisfactory especially if tested after completion to a pressure of 3 p.s.i.

Most importantly the filler to the tank should be so arranged that any spillage or overflow goes overboard and not into the boat. This is vital in a petrol-engined boat but still very desirable in a diesel installation. A deck filler is the best arrangement. Tanks over about 10 gallons in capacity should have a separate vent, again leading to the outside of the boat. Rubber hose leading from the deck filler to the tank connection should be held on with hose clips. A common fault with the filling arrangement is that the diameter of the deck filler and hose leading to the tank is too small to take the full flow from a fuel bowser so fuel bubbles back all over the deck. To avoid this the inside diameter should be at least 2 inches.

It is the propeller thrusting against the propeller shaft that makes the boat go along. Marine gearboxes are designed to take this load. If the engine is solidly mounted it must be aligned extremely carefully with the propeller shaft. This alignment must be checked regularly especially in a wooden boat and when the boat is put into the water after a winter ashore. Excessive vibration and wear of the stern tube and gearbox bearings will take place if the engine is misaligned. A flexibly mounted engine must have a flexible drive. The usual method (Figure 46) with a single flexible coupling

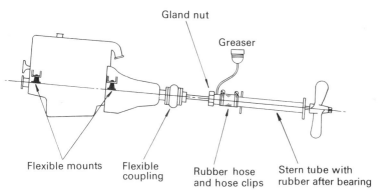

Gland nut

Greaser

Flexible mounts

Flexible coupling

Rubber hose and hose clips

Stern tube with rubber after bearing

46   A common method of providing a flexible drive. The flexible
stern tube connection allows sideways movement

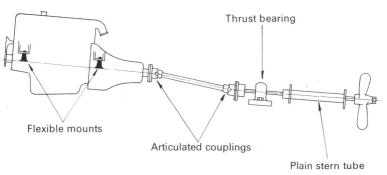

Thrust bearing

Flexible mounts

Articulated couplings

Plain stern tube

47   A fully floating engine with articulated drive

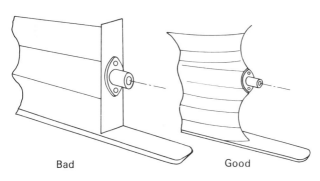

Bad

Good

8   Good and bad keel endings

requires a flexibly-attached forward bearing on the stern tube because flexible couplings do not tolerate much movement in a lateral plane. Their main function is to provide angular flexibility. With universal joints, a thrust bearing is required to take out the propeller thrust from the shaft line before it reaches the aftermost joint (Figure 47).

A thick square-cut end to the keel immediately in front of the propeller often causes much vibration from the aft end of the boat. The keel or deadwood should be tapered to a point above and below the shaft (Figure 48).

The battery will need regular topping-up so it should be reasonably accessible. It should also be well secured against the chance of falling over on its side and spilling acid into the bilge. In fast boats it should be strapped down. It should also be in a well ventilated area because explosive gases are given off during charging. The electrical system serving the engine will be unfused while all the other cables leading to lights, screen wipers etc., should be fused from a small fuse box. This should be easily accessible. A neat arrangement is provided by a combined fuse and switch panel fitted at the steering position. Wiring should be neatly laid out and clipped in place every few inches. Wires straggling over the engine are a sign of poor electrical workmanship. Most desirable—even on the smallest boat—is a master switch to isolate the battery, otherwise an electrical fault may cause a fire while the boat is idle during the week. A battery switch also reduces the chance of electrolytic action in the stern gear due to electrical leakages. Turning off this switch, the petrol tap and the engine and toilet seacocks, safely shuts down the boat for the week.

Noise
A quiet engine installation is achieved by fitting flexible mounts, sealing the engine in an air-tight box, and lining the inside of the box with noise absorbing material. Flexible mounts were discussed earlier. Sealing the engine box needs some explanation. Noise leaks out of holes in an engine box just as water leaks out of a hole in a pipe. A small hole leaks a disproportionate amount of noise. The engine needs to be completely encased—below the floorboards as well as above

The best way to do this is to mould-in a tray underneath the engine which marries up with a hinged box cover fitting over the engine. Any holes, for instance where the gear lever or exhaust pipe passes through, should be sealed with rubber gromets or close fitting plates.

Enclosing the engine like this of course deprives it of air. Air is required for combustion and also for general cooling, so air inlets are essential. To stop the noise leaking out through these inlets a noise trap should be fitted (working on the principle of a labyrinth lined with noise absorbing material) or alternatively large diameter ducts leading to ventilators on the side decks or transom. An electric fan may be necessary to create an air flow, and is essential in a petrol-engined installation enclosed like this. Just before starting the engine the fan should be switched on for a minute to clear away any possible petrol fumes. On a petrol installation it is essential that the fan is spark-proof and that it sucks air *out* of the compartment. With a diesel, the fan should blow air *in*. On the subject of ventilation, engine smells can be virtually eliminated if the crankcase breather is vented into the engine intake.

The third important method of noise reduction is lining the interior surfaces of the engine box with noise absorbing material such as polyurethane foam, glass fibre mat or rock wool. Inflammable materials should be avoided especially with petrol engines. To protect the lining, perforated metal is often fitted over the material. Usually noise-absorbing material is the most evident of any noise reduction measures taken, but it is only a part of what should be done. Many boats have no noise insulation at all, others merely have some glass wool inside the engine case. Noise is tiresome after a time and it is well worth the small extra cost to quieten a noisy high-revving diesel.

If an engine loses oil pressure, for instance because of a broken oil pipe, or overheats because of a water pump failure, it will quickly grind to an expensive halt. An oil pressure gauge and a water temperature gauge or warning lights are therefore important instruments. To indicate loss of battery charging, a charging light or an ammeter, or better still a voltmeter, should be fitted. Loss of charge will eventually mean a flat battery. A rev counter (tachometer) is very useful for fast boats to check on engine performance and propeller matching. Some means of measuring how much fuel there is in the tank is essential. A dip stick is a reliable measure, while a gauge is more convenient, although it may at some time go wrong and give a misleading reading. This may lead to a dangerous situation at sea so spare fuel should always be carried.

Outboards

The advantages of an outboard lie in its light weight, its portability and that it causes little intrusion inside the boat. A 60 h.p. motor weighs about 200 lb. Compare this with the two inboard engines discussed earlier—325 lb (petrol) and 625 lb (diesel). In fact the disparity is even greater because these latter weights do not take into account installation gear—stern gear, battery, engine casing etc. A 60 h.p. outboard costs between £600 and £700. This lies somewhat above the equivalent inboard petrol engine, but again there is the extra cost of installation of the inboard.

The lightness of the outboard is achieved by adopting the 2-stroke cycle (power stroke every revolution) and by designing the engine to run at high revs (5000–6000 r.p.m.). Outboards make excellent power units for small planing cruisers. For planing boats over about 22 ft in length their advantages die out because the extra weight of a petrol inboard ceases to be so important, while the running costs of large outboards begin to be appreciably greater. For displacement boats an outboard is rarely satisfactory compared with an inboard, especially on cruisers larger than about 20 ft (seagoing) and 25 ft (inland). The popular makes of outboard are primarily designed for fast runabouts. They have small high-revving propellers and every effort is made to reduce weight and to tune the engines to peak at the highest horsepower. For instance the 55 h.p. Chrysler achieves its power at 5250 r.p.m. and has a twin cylinder engine of 730 cc. This represents 76 h.p. per litre—a very high performance (compare it with your car).

The engine drives a $10\frac{3}{8}$ in diameter propeller at 3250 r.p.m. These high propeller revs are only suitable for planing boats. For displacement boats the revs are far too high for good efficiency. For speeds up to 7 or 8 knots propeller revs should be less than 2000 which entails using a much larger propeller. A small propeller means a relatively poor performance and a high fuel consumption.

Smaller outboards are often used on inland cruisers. The same arguments about propeller revs apply to small outboards, but despite the propeller inefficiency the actual fuel consumption is not great. For instance a 24 ft canal cruiser is just adequately powered by a 6 h.p. motor which will consume about $\frac{1}{2}$ gallon an hour of petrol/oil mixture. This makes cruising reasonably inexpensive. If the mistake is made of fitting a much larger engine the fuel consumption will be much greater.

A 40 h.p. Johnson weighs about 130 lb and this approaches the limit of easy portability. It would be quite easy to take this outboard home for the winter for preservation and maintenance. Because outboards are fairly easily taken off a boat one has to cater for the possibility of theft—indeed, insurance companies require that approved locking devices are fitted. The transom has to have a cut-out to allow the outboard to be mounted low enough. In order to stop a wave flooding into the boat over the low transom, an outboard well has to be fitted (Figure 49). This well should be watertight and self-draining, i.e. with a sloping bottom and drain holes in the transom. This well takes up quite a large amount of space because it has to be long enough to allow the motor to tilt. To accommodate a motor of up to 55 h.p. it should be $21\frac{1}{2}$ in long from the transom to the forward bulkhead, while for engines between 56 and 90 h.p. this dimension should be 24 in. The larger wells would in fact accommodate an outdrive engine so one of the advantages of an outboard is lost.

Apart from this snag an outboard has several inherent disadvantages. It is high revving and the buzzing noise becomes irritating after a time, especially on a displacement or inland cruiser. The engine has to run at around 3000 r.p.m. to achieve a reasonable cruising speed. If a larger engine is fitted and run more slowly the fuel consumption will suffer and the plugs will be inclined to foul. On a fast boat the buzz is in keeping with the rate of progress, and in any case the wind and water noises tend to drown the noise of the outboard, but at canal speeds it is irritating. Although the modern outboard buzzes, the loudness is really quite low. Johnson, Evinrude, Chrysler, Mercury, Penta, Crescent and Yamaha are good examples.

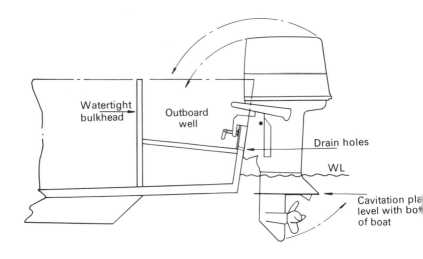

49 *An outboard installation. The outboard should sit vertically using the adjustment rack provided*

These engines in particular have overcome the traditional objections to outboards, namely, noise and unreliability. The modern ignition systems have a great deal to do with the better reliability. Many outboards have capacitor-discharge ignition (no contact breakers) and a really waterproofed system. They run on 50:1 petrol/oil mixture which reduces plug fouling and gives a cleaner exhaust, although this is usually discharged underwater anyway.

Not only do outboards use more fuel than automotive-based petrol engines, but there is the oil to add as well. On the other hand only low octane petrol is required; in the UK this means 2-star petrol. A 60 h.p. outboard will consume about $5\frac{1}{2}$ gallons an hour at full throttle reducing to about half of this at around 3500 r.p.m. This can be compared with about $3\frac{3}{4}$ gallons an hour (full throttle) for a 4-stroke automotive petrol engine and about 3 gallons an hour for a diesel.

Outboard-powered boats do not steer well at low speeds. There is virtually no rudder effect when in neutral. Because the propeller is relatively small and situated aft of the transom, thrust is lost to a greater extent in a seaway at lower speeds than with an inboard. The outboard is less seaworthy both in this sense and in the sense that it is open to the elements.

It is easy to carry a spare outboard. In fact rather than have one large engine a very neat and logical arrangement is to have two smaller outboards of the same total power. Although two 20 h.p. engines will cost more than one 40 h.p. there will be great sea-going confidence, twin-engine manoeuvrability and the smaller motors will be easier to take home for the winter. Also when cruising slowly for long periods, running one small outboard will return a much better fuel consumption than running one large one.

Electric starting and charging is usually only available on outboards greater than about 20 h.p. For cruising, interior lights will be required and the starting battery should be able to cope. On outboard-powered inland craft where less than 20 h.p. is quite adequate power, there is the problem of how to provide electricity. One or two outboard manufacturers do make small electric start outboards, for instance, Chrysler (9·9 h.p. and 12·9 h.p.) and Penta (9 h.p. and 14 h.p.). In some cases the r.p.m. at which battery charging commences is rather high (3500) and this may be too fast for an inland cruiser. In other words the wash created may be too much. The larger the outboard chosen the more serious this becomes. For instance a 20 h.p. engine on a 20 ft inland cruiser would certainly encounter this problem.

The maintenance of an outboard is quite simple especially if it can be done at home in the garage. There is the gear hub to keep filled with a special oil, linkages and pivots to keep greased and in the less modern outboards the contact breakers and plugs to clean and replace. Modern outboards with CD ignition and surface gap sparking plugs need less attention. On the other hand if something goes wrong with CD ignition it is a job for the dealer. Salt water tends to corrode outboards and at the end of the season the engine should be run in fresh water for a few minutes and washed off on the outside. The fuel filters should also be regularly cleaned.

When choosing an outboard there is little difference between the major makes in respect of weight, price or fuel consumption. Technically the engines are similar. However, the reduction ratio varies considerably and except for boats faster than about 20 knots it is worth checking. The gear ratio is usually given in terms of the number of teeth on the gear wheels, e.g. 13:26. This is a 2:1 reduction ratio the propeller turns at half the speed of the engine, and this is quite a good ratio. Anything less than $1\frac{1}{2}$:1 is very poor and should not be chosen for anticipated speeds of less than 8 knots. The variation within the range of any one manufacturer is surprising. For instance, the Johnson 6 h.p. has a 15:26 ratio (1·75:1) while the Johnson 50 h.p. has an excellent ratio of 2·67:1. The difference in performance which the reduction ratio makes is very noticeable. Fuel consumption is also better for a high ratio.

There are one or two 4-stroke outboards available. The advantages of this type of cycle are that the fuel consumption is better, the plugs do not foul up so quickly and the exhaust is cleaner. The engine burns neat petrol so there is no mixing to do and the fuel consumption is more comparable to an automotive petrol engine. There is the Bearcat 55 h.p. outboard which weighs and costs considerably more than the equivalent 2-stroke outboard. Lower down in the range the Honda 7·5 h.p. weighs and costs much the same as an equivalent 2-stroke.

Paraffin outboards are another alternative. A few of the Yamaha range operate on a paraffin/oil mixture, considerably reducing the running costs. On the other hand, plug and cylinder fouling is increased and they have to be started on petrol and switched over when warm. The bi-fuel system is all arranged inside the head and is quite easy to use.

Outdrives

An outdrive arrangement (Figure 50), otherwise called an inboard-outboard or Z drive, dispenses with the gearbox (ahead and astern gears are incorporated in the bevel gears) and enables the engine to be tucked right aft up against the transom. Thus the advantages of both an inboard and an

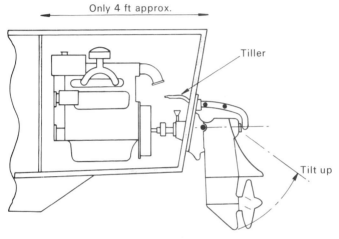

50 An outdrive fits very neatly in a transom-sterned boat

outboard are achieved. The engine noise is further away from the helmsman and the cabin, and there is no engine box disrupting the cabin/cockpit layout. There is no gland to leak and, as the leg and propeller can be tilted out of the water, it is an easy matter to disentangle weed and polythene bags. This facility also enables a shallow draft boat to run up to a beach or take the ground. If the leg meets an obstruction it will kick up automatically. If the leg touches a sandy bottom the propeller will probably be damaged—only on a very hard bottom does the little skeg give protection. The only maintenance required is to refill the gearcase with oil, and grease the pivots and linkages. Installation costs are probably less, which offsets the extra cost of the outdrive itself compared to a gearbox, so that an outdrive-powered boat is usually no more expensive than one inboard-powered.

Naturally there are snags involved. The greatest of these is the lack of steering effect at low speeds. In fact the leg is a poor rudder and to permit steering one must keep the propeller turning. Manoeuvres must be made in a bolder fashion. Other remarks about steering are made in Chapter 10. The gear ratios adopted in outdrives are usually lower than conventional inboard ratios. Outdrives, like outboards, are primarily designed for fast boats, so the comments made on the lack of propeller efficiency and seaworthiness of outboards apply also to outdrives, albeit to a lesser extent. Despite these disadvantages outdrives are an obvious choice for planing cruisers of all sizes. The installation is neat and gives the greatest freedom in cabin and cockpit layouts.

Jets

Many of the advantages of an outdrive apply to a jet drive. The engine is tucked right aft and needs no gearbox. Reverse is achieved by a 'bucket' arrangement which deflects the water issuing from the jet orifice, forward, under the hull (Figure 51). Manoeuvrability at speed and acceleration and deceleration are phenomenal. Steering at low speeds is also very positive. The impeller is hidden inside the jet unit which makes it

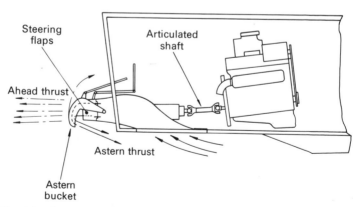

51   A jet drive is good for small planing boats but not very good for slow sea-going cruisers

a very safe type of propulsion if the boat is to be taken among swimmers or water-skiers. In the case of a planing boat the efficiency of a jet drive, i.e. the performance of the boat, is just as good as that of an inboard. On the other hand jet drives in displacement boats give a noticeably poorer performance. At sea this would be especially marked. On inland waters a jet does have the advantage of being less prone to clogging with weed if a grill is fitted over the intake.

Other drives

A 'vee' drive (Figure 52) gives the advantage of an outdrive in that the engine can be placed well aft while having the better steering characteristics of an inboard. The only disadvantage is the extra cost of the actual vee-drive gearbox. Borg Warner make a vee drive integral with their gearbox but the cost is high.

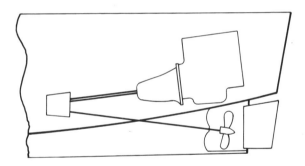

52   A vee drive arrangement

Hydraulic drive or as it is sometimes called, hydrostatic drive, enables the engine to be placed wherever convenient, because the only connections between the engine and the propeller shaft are flexible hydraulic hoses. The engine drives a hydraulic pump which supplies oil under very high pressure to a hydraulic motor which turns the propeller shaft. The engine can be tucked away, for instance across the transom in a noise-tight compartment. Control is achieved hydraulically by reversing the flow of oil. Ahead or astern can be selected instantaneously at any engine speed. The disadvantages are the high cost, the loss of power in the hydraulics and the necessity to match the engine, pump, motor and propeller carefully. Assuming the design of the system is done correctly the loss of power is typically at least 15 per cent and in some systems 30 per cent. If the system is not matched, particularly if the propeller is the wrong size, the power capable of being transmitted to the propeller at full throttle may only be a fraction of the maximum power of the engine. There have been many disappointed boat owners on this account and also because the oil has been inadequately cooled. The oil must be cooled and filtered and appropriate equipment should be included in the hydraulic system together with a reservoir tank.

Variable-pitch propellers, like the vee drive and hydraulic drive, are only occasionally used in motor cruisers. The blades on a VP propeller are adjustable in pitch, the control being taken up the propeller shaft to a lever inside the boat. Astern is achieved by reversing the pitch. Naturally the control and manoeuvrability of a boat so fitted is excellent, although it is sometimes difficult to achieve an exact neutral with the propeller still turning round. No gearbox or clutch is fitted. Unfortunately a reduction gear is required for engines other than those which run slowly, such as the Sabb (which can be supplied with a VP propeller). If a gearbox is also required the cost becomes, of course, much greater than for a conventional drive.

7 How Much Power?

A boat can be over-powered or under-powered depending on its hull shape and where it is to be used. Choosing a sensible engine power is often difficult. A related question is, how fast will she go? and this chapter is intended to give guidance on both these points.

Minimum power

A sea-going cruiser must have a reserve of power to cope with strong head winds, choppy seas and tidal currents. The power needed to punch into wind and sea can easily be double that needed for calm water. Therefore, depending on the size of boat, there is a certain minimum engine power that common sense suggests. Apart from the size of boat there are other factors to take into account. Different localities have different tidal streams and wind conditions; different engines and drives give different thrusts at the propeller. The propellers of outboards and outdrives are more affected by severe pitching motion than those of inboards. Small fast-revving propellers such as those fitted to outboards are less efficient than large slow-running ones absorbing the same horsepower. The actual horsepower produced at the propeller by the typical outboard is less than its nominal horsepower suggests and is usually less than the actual horsepower produced by an inboard engine of the same nominal power. The curves given for minimum horsepower (Figure 53) therefore distinguish between inboards and outboards, but even so, other factors have not been taken into account and the curves should only be treated as an indicative guide and not as a precise statement.

The minimum engine horsepower talked about so far will

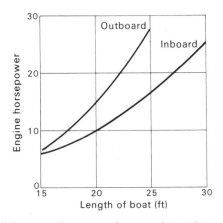

53   Sensible minimum engine powers for sea-going cruisers

only give displacement speeds but there is such a thing as minimum power for a planing boat—the minimum power necessary to plane. To own a planing cruiser whose engine is not quite powerful enough to make her plane, or only just powerful enough in the right conditions, is most frustrating. It is well to err on the over-powerful side in order that the hump can be got over easily, while giving a margin for occasions when extra passengers are on board or when the bottom of the boat is fouled. The power:weight ratio of the boat and engine combination is the most important factor with the shape of the hull coming second. The bare minimum is about 50 h.p. per ton but medium or deep vee hulls require a higher figure. Over 100 h.p. per ton will give a very lively performance with any type of planing hull form and should give speed:length ratios of over 5 (Figure 12).

Maximum power

With outboard-powered cruisers on inland waters there is definitely a maximum sensible power to choose. An outboard which is too large has to be run slowly and consequently will be thirsty on fuel and may have a tendency to foul the plugs continually. Speeds on inland waters are often restricted by

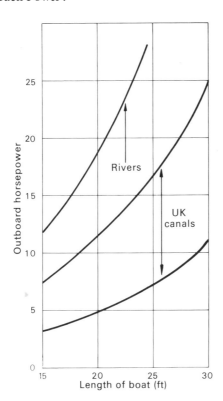

54   Sensible outboard powers for inland cruisers

law and undue wash is a nuisance to other users of the waterway besides eroding the banks. The curves given (Figure 54)
are again only intended as a guide to a suitable horsepower.

A large inboard petrol or diesel engine is also out of place
on inland waters, but running such engines slowly does not
give rise to the same extent to the problems associated with
running outboards slowly.

The limit to the installed horsepower at sea is set by the type
of hull shape. As mentioned in Chapter 8, to over-power a
displacement cruiser is to waste fuel and money for only a
very slight increase in speed. Thus it is possible to draw a
sensible line of maximum horsepower for various sizes of
displacement cruiser (Figure 55). In the case of a diesel or
petrol inboard displacement cruiser, fitting an engine larger

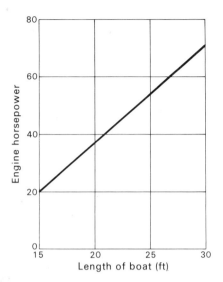

55 Sensible maximum power for a sea-going displacement cruiser

than that shown on the curve has its advantages and disadvantages. The engine will cost more initially and will take up more room. On the other hand to reach say 6 knots it will be running more slowly and possibly more quietly while only consuming a little more fuel. There will be more reserve of power to counter heavy weather and the weight of the engine will be no disadvantage. For normal purposes the maximum power given in the curve in Figure 55 should give ample reserve of power.

How fast will she go?

Boat builders' speed figures are often optimistic, especially for displacement cruisers. With planing boats the speeds quoted are often measured speeds and are more reliable.

The easiest way to estimate the speed of a displacement boat is to consider the speed:length ratio she is likely to achieve. A true, heavy-displacement hull form is unlikely to exceed a speed:length ratio of 1·5 i.e. 1·5 times the square root of the waterline length (in feet). If the hull has a flat bottom aft, the buttock lines running nearly horizontally to a wide transom stern, then a speed:length ratio of 2 or $2\frac{1}{2}$ may be reached if a large engine for the size of boat is fitted—for example, a 70 h.p. diesel in a 22 ft boat. At these speeds the power:weight ratio comes into play and the curves in Figure 12 will give an idea of the speed:length ratio to expect. The true fast round-bilge form will give speed:length ratios of up to 3 or 4 with the appropriate power:weight ratio. For example, a 21 ft fast round-bilge cruiser weighing about a ton with a 40 h.p. diesel (a light automative type) has a power:weight ratio of 40 which allows a speed:length ratio of almost 3 (Figure 12) giving a speed of 12 knots.

Knowing the length, all-up weight and engine power of a boat and having classified the hull shape into a category, heavy displacement, light transom-sterned displacement, or fast round-bilge, a good estimate of the speed can be obtained from the speed:length ratio and the curves drawn in Figure 12.

The speed of a planing boat is largely a matter of the power:weight ratio, the length of the hull being of lesser importance. A simple and reliable formula relates speed to the power:weight ratio, making allowance for other variables by a factor K

$$\text{Speed (knots)} = K \sqrt{\frac{\text{h.p.}}{\text{Weight (tons)}}}$$

This is commonly called the Barnaby formula. The value of K depends on how efficiently the hull planes. This not only depends on the length and hull shape but on the actual speed achieved. At speeds when the hull is only just planing the value of K is low—between 2·0 and 2·5. Deeper veed hulls will also give lower values of K (little more than 2·0) until a speed:length ratio of almost 5 is reached. Above these speeds the value of K for modern motor cruisers lies between 2·6 and 3·0, whether their hulls are deep vee or shallow vee. Fast round-bilge hulls give K values of 2·0–2·5.

One can see from this formula the effect of fitting a larger engine. Unlike a displacement boat which gives little increase in speed for greater horsepower, a planing boat responds well, providing the weight is not increased significantly. The speed will be increased by the square root of the power—doubling the power will increase the speed 1·4 times. By fitting a larger engine one is increasing the power:weight ratio.

Horsepower and propellers

The actual horsepower produced by an engine and the efficiency with which the propeller turns this power into thrust is of importance in the context of speed and powering. Unfortunately there is a variety of standards by which engines are rated. Between the crankshaft and the propeller there are many small sources of loss of the power produced by the engine. There are losses due to back pressure caused by the exhaust system and the intake filter, power is absorbed by the dynamo and water pump, and there are frictional losses in the gearbox or outdrive and the shaft bearings. Altogether these represent 10–20 per cent of the gross power produced. Also a high air temperature or a low barometric pressure reduces the power output.

The most honest horsepower rating that can be given for a marine engine is one where the power is measured at the propeller shaft coupling with the engine complete with all the normal power-absorbing accessories and at a specified air temperature and pressure. The term SHP (shaft horsepower) usually implies this type of rating. Normally, a continuous and a maximum (usually for one hour) rating is given. Diesels are often rated in this way, for example the Perkins and Mercedes.

Besides SHP the common recognised standards for engine rating are BS (British Standard), DIN (German), BIA and SAE (American). BS 765 and 649 and DIN 6270 standards are not specifically for marine engines but at least they are net powers produced under realistic conditions. A continuous and a maximum rating are specified. The BIA standard is used for outboard engines and the standard specifies only a short duration of test, the power being measured at the crankshaft, so the actual power delivered to the propeller is somewhat less in service. However, most makes of outboards are rated to BIA or similar standards, so comparisons between different makes can be made.

The SAE code is really a sprint rating of the bare engine and in practice gives an optimistic figure—optimistic by about 25 per cent.

As an example of how the different ratings show up on one particular engine, consider the Perkins 4107 diesel:

SHP max	47
SHP continuous	36
DIN max	46
DIN continuous	35·5
SAE	58

It is mentioned in several contexts in this book that a large slow-turning propeller is more efficient than a small fast-revving one. This fact becomes more and more important the lower the potential maximum speed of the boat. In other words displacement boats will benefit greatly by a reduction ratio between the engine and the propeller. Full throttle propeller revs should be less than 2000 r.p.m. and preferably less than 1000 r.p.m. The gain in propeller efficiency means that more thrust is produced. For example, consider a 20 h.p. engine in a 25 ft cruiser. If the engine develops its power at 3500 r.p.m. then the small propeller resulting from a direct drive gearbox will only be 34 per cent efficient. The propeller will be slipping badly. 2:1 will give 42 per cent and 3:1 47 per cent efficiency. The greater the reduction ratio and the larger the propeller the less slippage will take place. Direct drive will result in only 6·8 h.p. actually being used to drive the boat, while 3:1 reduction (shaft revs 1170 r.p.m.) will result in 9·4 h.p. being used, which is a 40 per cent increase in effective power. This will mean slightly more speed and much better performance when plugging into strong winds and choppy water, besides giving greater astern power. The smaller the engine the more important it is to use the power efficiently. If this boat had a 10 h.p. engine obviously a very efficient propeller would be even more advantageous in order to make the most of the small horsepower available.

Propellers work more efficiently at higher boat speeds and, in the case of planing boats, over 50 per cent efficiency is easily obtained without having to restrict the propeller r.p.m. to below 2000. In fact 3000 r.p.m. is quite in order at speeds over 20 knots. Hence outboards and outdrives usually only incorporate 1·5:1 to 2:1 reduction ratios because both are really designed for fast boats and not slow speed work. Used on a displacement boat one has to accept that performance will be curtailed compared with an inboard drive where the propeller shaft r.p.m. is less. For fast craft the outboard and the outdrive give less appendage drag and a more horizontal thrust compared with an inboard. There is neither rudder, nor inclined shaft, nor shaft brackets to create parasitic drag. The legs protruding into the water are streamlined to minimise drag.

To sum up, displacement boats need large slow-revving propellers, while planing boats can achieve good efficiency with smaller propellers despite the fact that greater horsepower is being handled. In general the propeller itself is still the best way of propelling a boat. The jet drive gives as good a performance in planing boats but a markedly lesser efficiency in displacement craft.

8 Fuel Consumption

What is likely to be the fuel consumption of a particular combination of cruiser and engine? This question is likely to become more and more important as the cost of fuel increases. The salesman may not be able to give you exact figures, while engine manufacturers sometimes give only a guide. If a fast, petrol-engined cruiser is contemplated the fuel costs can be staggering and may amount to a large proportion of the cost of maintaining the boat. The facts given in this chapter should give an idea of what to expect.

There are two ways of expressing fuel consumption—in terms of gallons per hour and in terms of miles per gallon (m.p.g.). Because knots are the normal measure of speed, m.p.g.—in respect of a boat—is calculated in nautical miles per gallon (a nautical mile is 6080 ft; a land mile is 5280 ft; or 1 nautical mile = 1·15 land miles). If your cruising is to be mainly in the form of days on the water, perhaps a trip up the river and back, then fuel consumption in terms of gallons (or fractions of a gallon) an hour will be more appropriate than m.p.g. The actual mileage covered is of no importance, there being no actual destination. On the other hand serious cruising at sea, or perhaps a definite cruise on the canals from A to B, makes m.p.g. more appropriate.

Estimating the probable consumption in gallons an hour is fairly easy. It is entirely a function of the engine—the boat playing no part at all. The engine produces power which makes one boat go at 6 knots and another at 10 knots, depending on the hull size and shape, but the fuel consumed is largely a matter of the power being produced. Similar engines of different makes have very similar consumptions. For instance, a Ford diesel will have much the same consumption as a Volvo or Renault or Perkins diesel when producing the same power, i.e. they are approximately equally efficient in burning the fuel. There may be a difference of perhaps 25 per cent but certainly not of 100 per cent. Similarly, various 4-stroke petrol engines are comparable and so too are outboards, so one can draw up a table for the various types of engine, based on each horsepower produced, as follows:

	Pints per h.p. per hour
Automotive diesels	0·4–0·45
Small true marine diesels (up to about 15 h.p.)	0·45 0·5
4-stroke automotive petrol engines	0·5–0·55
2-stroke inboard true marine petrol engines	approx. 1·0
2-stroke outboards under 10 h.p.	1·0
around 20 h.p.	0·85
around 40 h.p.	0·8
above 60 h.p.	0·7

These figures are applicable only in conjunction with the manufacturers' maximum horsepower. For instance the Mercedes OM 636 diesel develops 40 horsepower and so, at full throttle, the consumption is 40 h.p. × 0·4 pints/h.p./hour = 16 pints per hour = 2 gallons an hour.

With the above figures one can make a good stab at the full throttle consumption, but honest horsepower must be used, for instance SHP, BS or DIN standard powers. Using the SAE code will give a higher figure for consumption than will be realised in practice. In the case of outboards BIA horsepower or equivalent should be used.

This is not the whole story however. An engine only works at its most efficient at or near full throttle. In a boat the load on the engine drops off rapidly at lower throttle openings and the process of combustion is less efficient. This means that for every horsepower produced more fuel is consumed. Some engines become inefficient at low throttle openings. Outboards are particularly bad from this point of view (this is why the plugs tend to soot up), diesels are good and 4-stroke petrol engines come somewhere in between. The actual figures for pints per horsepower can be put into graph form (Figure 56). Some engine manufacturers give apparently similar curves for their engines, but these are invariably based on full throttle operation, varying the r.p.m. by varying the load on the engine. The curves in Figure 56 relate to use in a boat.

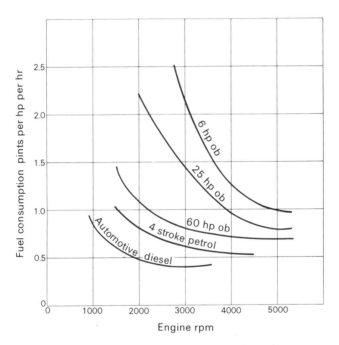

56   Fuel consumption per horsepower of various engines when throttled back

In fact Figure 56 is not of much practical use because one never knows how much power the engine will be developing at normal cruising speed. Full throttle consumption is one thing but not many people ordinarily run a boat at full throttle (which is inadvisable in any case). As speed is reduced the power developed by the engine is reduced much more rapidly than pro rata. In fact, with a displacement boat the power needed to drive the boat decreases as (speed)^3 or (speed)^4, while with planing boats it reduces as (speed)^2 or (speed)^3. The fuel consumption curve, however, does not exactly follow this power law because of the reduced engine efficiency at lower revs. As a general guide, outboards reduce their fuel consumption roughly in relation to their r.p.m. Thus at an r.p.m. of about 3000 the fuel consumption will be half that at full throttle as calculated from the figures given earlier for pints/h.p./hour. The more efficient diesel or 4-stroke petrol engine consume much less than half the full throttle consumption at half r.p.m. In fact the consumption will be about a third to a fifth.

The fuel consumption under cruising conditions will depend very much on where one sets the throttle. It is easy to be wasteful of fuel when running a motor cruiser. The tendency is to open the throttle too much. There are distinct speeds at which the best economy is obtained. With a displacement boat it is at a speed:length ratio between about 1·1 and 1·3 and with a planing boat, on the plane, it is at a speed:length ratio between 3·5 and 5, i.e. properly on the plane but not by any means flat out. In fact the trick is to throttle back and, as soon as the bows start to rise and one feels the boat beginning to drag, the optimum point has been passed. The best speed is where the boat is still level and fast, and just above the throttle opening at which she will start to fall off the plane.

With a displacement boat it is simply a matter of cruising between the speed:length ratios mentioned. Large humpy waves behind the transom and steep diagonal waves from the bows mean that she is going too fast.

To sum up how to estimate the likely cruising fuel consumption in gallons per hour, here are a few statements:

(i) With an outboard-powered boat one can bank on the cruising consumption being about half the full throttle consumption (but see (iv)).

(ii) A displacement cruiser with an inboard engine will cruise at one-quarter of the full throttle fuel consumption providing the speed is kept well below the hump.

(iii) A high powered planing cruiser will be able to cruise (planing) at one-half the full throttle fuel consumption.

(iv) If the power: weight ratio is not very great in a planing cruiser, for example, a 60 h.p. engine in a 22 footer only giving perhaps 18 knots, then the throttle cannot be reduced much from full throttle before the boat falls off the plane.

Miles per gallon

The m.p.g. achieved by a cruiser involves the characteristics of the boat as well as the engine. At a given fuel consumption one has to know how fast the boat will go. The figure for speed, in knots, divided by the fuel consumption in gallons an hour gives nautical m.p.g. We are all familiar with the m.p.g. of the motor-car. A car that only does 20 m.p.g. is considered thirsty. With boats one is lucky to get 10 m.p.g. Large fast planing boats may consume a gallon for every mile covered.

With displacement boats the faster one goes the less the m.p.g. achieved. In the case of planing boats there is a region of comparatively good m.p.g. at moderate planing speeds—in fact the speed:length ratios mentioned earlier. A slightly better m.p.g. is usually achieved off the plane and running slowly but the improvement is not great. Large powerful engines do not produce horsepower very efficiently when ticking over and this offsets the greatly reduced horsepower requirement of the boat. In other words, one might just as well cruise on the plane as off as far as fuel consumption is concerned.

Fast round-bilge craft, because the speed is obtained almost by brute force rather than by planing, do not give good m.p.g. figures. The m.p.g. gradually falls as the speed increases, but not to such a great extent as for a true displacement boat.

To achieve a high m.p.g. the boat should be easily driven, which means a long, light, thin hull powered by a small economical diesel at the quiet unfussy speeds of 1·1 speed:length ratio. For instance, a 25 ft cruiser weighing less than one ton with a round-bilge form and a narrowish beam of 7 ft 6 in and without drag-inducing devices such as bilge keels and large rudders, should do $5\frac{1}{2}$ knots in calm water with a 5 h.p. diesel. This would involve a consumption of 2 pints an hour, so a gallon would last 4 hours, in which time the boat would travel 22 miles—a very good performance. Even in this example the limit of practicability is reached. At sea a 5 h.p. engine would be insufficiently powerful and bilge keels would be desirable but this sort of m.p.g. can be achieved on inland waters. More speed can only be at the expense of m.p.g.: any planing boat is lucky to reach 5 m.p.g.

Typical examples

The following examples of typical cruisers illustrate the great range of fuel consumptions possible:

(i) 18 ft, hard-chine, 2-berth cruiser powered by a 60 h.p. outboard. This has a top speed of 25 knots and a corresponding fuel consumption of 5·4 gallons an hour (Figure 57). Throttling back to 17 knots improves the m.p.g. and the consumption drops to 3 gallons an hour—a considerable improvement. The m.p.g. curve shows a characteristic common with planing boats. When the boat is struggling onto the plane at 5–10 knots the m.p.g. drops markedly. This is the inefficient

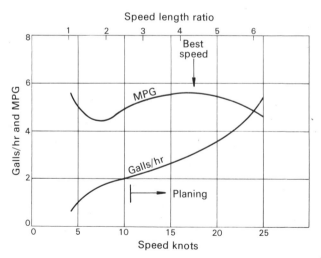

57   18 ft cruiser with a 60 h.p. outboard

zone of hull performance. As soon as planing commences the m.p.g. rises and then falls off at full throttle. With a fast boat like this the correct propeller size is important. The correct propeller is one which allows the revs at full throttle to reach the manufacturer's recommended figure—usually around 5000 r.p.m. Too large or too small a propeller reduces the top speed and causes the consumption to rise at higher speeds.

(ii) 22 ft displacement cruiser weighing about 2 tons and powered by a 40 h.p. inboard engine. The curves in Figure 58 give the performance for both a petrol inboard and a diesel.

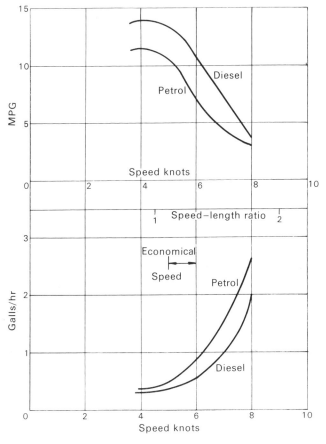

58   22 ft displacement cruiser with a 40 h.p. inboard engine

In both cases the consumptions rise steeply at speeds over 6 knots with a corresponding drop in m.p.g. At a good economical speed of 5½ knots there is little wash; the diesel boat goes for 12½ miles on a gallon and the petrol boat 9 miles. These curves show how foolish it is to push the throttle too far forward on a displacement cruiser—in return for very little extra speed the noise, wash and fuel consumption increase enormously.

(iii) 24 ft inland cruiser with a hard-chine hull of shallow draft powered by (a) a 6 h.p. diesel and (b) a 6 h.p. outboard. Consumption is small at any speed by any standard—even the relatively thirsty outboard consumes only ½ gallon an hour cruising (Figure 59). The small diesel gives the astonishing m.p.g. of 30 at 3·3 knots consuming less than a pint every hour. At this speed the speed:length ratio is less than 1·0 and the wash is like that of a rowing boat. This example is the rock

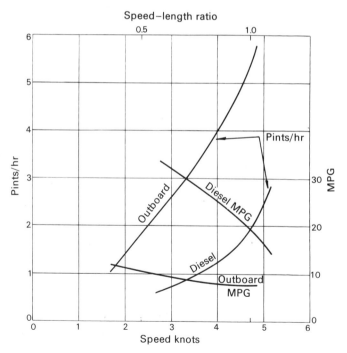

59   24 ft inland cruiser with a 6 h.p. engine

bottom end of the power and fuel consumption scale and shows how economical canal and river cruising can be, providing the engine chosen is not too large for the job.

(iv) 24 ft deep vee cruiser powered by twin 170 h.p. petrol outdrives. The full throttle consumption is 23 gallons an hour (Figure 60). On the other hand progress is very rapid and about

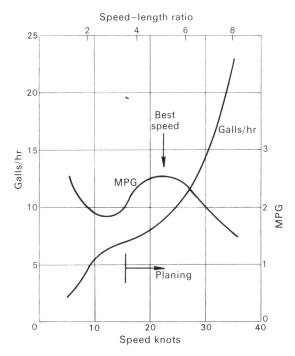

60   24 ft deep vee cruiser with twin 170 h.p. petrol outdrives

35 miles will have been covered in this time. Again the m.p.g. curve has a hump at 20–25 knots where the best cruising speed is obtained giving 2·5 m.p.g. In terms of cruising time, however, even the best planing speed consumes 8–10 gallons an hour.

(v) 29 ft fast round-bilge cruiser weighing $3\frac{1}{2}$ tons and powered by twin 78 h.p. diesels (Figure 61). At lower speeds a good m.p.g. is obtained (4–5) and taking into account the cheaper cost of diesel fuel the consumption at 12 knots cruising

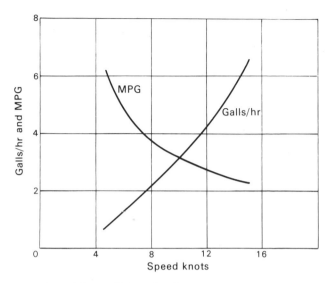

61   29 ft cruiser with twin 78 h.p. diesels

is very reasonable—$4\frac{1}{2}$ gallons an hour. This is the sort of cruiser in which long cruises can be contemplated with the seakindly motion of this hull form and yet a fast average speed.

Tank size

The tank capacity needs to be appropriate for the size of engine. A tank which is too small is a nuisance because it will need to be refilled frequently. The minimum practical, even with small engines, is about 6 gallons. This is just sufficient for an inland cruiser using about $\frac{1}{2}$ gallon an hour. Even inland refuelling stations are rather far apart and on the sea one must always allow ample fuel. Rough water and strong head winds and currents substantially decrease the speed and hence the m.p.g. If a cruise from A to B is contemplated it is wise to carry twice as much fuel as is theoretically necessary. It is also wise not to run a tank dry, otherwise the sediment at the bottom is likely to enter the fuel lines. Also, filling a tank to its utmost will result in a spillage over the deck so, although a tank may be say, 20 gallons nominal capacity, its actual working capacity is only perhaps 15–17 gallons. As a general guide the tank capacity should at least be sufficient for 12 hours running and preferably 24 hours. Very important is a reliable and easy method of checking the amount of fuel in the tank.

The larger the tank fitted the better but there is a limit, particularly for a planing boat, where weight is so important. Petrol weighs 7·2–7·5 lb per gallon and diesel 8·3–8.8 lb per gallon, so 100 gallons of fuel weigh 6 or 7 cwt. This sort of weight is, in any case, best sited in the bilges to help stability.

Two tanks are a great aid to safety, with a pipe system such that the engine can be fed from either tank. The chances of running out of fuel are much less and, if sediment causes a stoppage in the one tank, the engine can be switched over to the other. In any case tanks should be swilled out or, if they are large enough to have a manhole, they should be cleaned out every two years or so.

9 Stability

In the boat world the word stability is put to several uses—the steering of a boat can be stable, a boat is often said to be stable in a seaway and a boat can feel stable when one walks from side to side. This chapter is concerned with the last mentioned usage and, of more importance, the ability of a motor cruiser to recover from a large angle of heel. This sort of stability is a vital part of seaworthiness and is one of the basic and essential ingredients of a sea-going cruiser. Before anything else, a designer and the builder must ensure that the boat first floats, and then floats the right way up.

The reason a stable boat always returns to an even keel after being heeled over is shown in Figure 62. The position of the so-called centre of gravity of a boat—the combined centre of weight or mass of all the items comprising the craft—is fixed and does not move, whereas the position of the centre of the hole made in the water by the hull shifts around as the boat heels over and the immersed shape changes. As the boat heels the centre of buoyancy will slide sideways from under the centre of gravity, and, as the total weight and buoyancy force act through the CG and CB respectively, there is a leverage effect tending to right the craft i.e. the heeling force is being resisted.

If, with a small angle of heel, the centre of buoyancy moves rapidly to one side then the resisting lever—the stability—will be large. Someone walking around on board will feel that the boat is stiff and stable.

To be considered stable, a sea-going motor cruiser must be able to roll safely to very large angles of heel, so the shift of CB must continue beyond the first few degrees of heel. If the righting levers achieved at various angles of heel are plotted out as in Figure 62, a peak is achieved usually at around 40

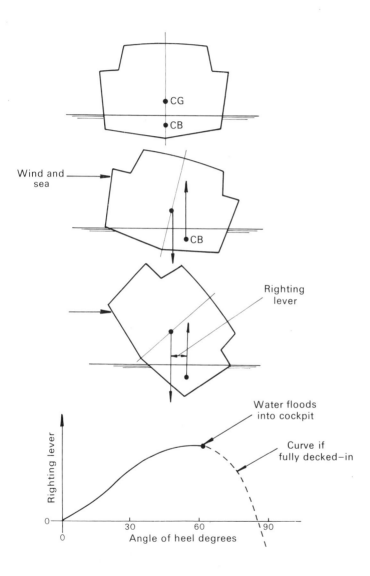

2   *Large angle stability*

of heel after which the lever drops away until eventually the CB is directly below the CG again and the boat capsizes.

The term metacentre often occurs when the subject of stability crops up. The metacentre is the point at which a vertical line through the CB crosses the centreline of the boat. The metacentric height is the distance between the CG and this point for small angles of heel. The larger the metacentric height the more stable the boat—at small angles of heel—but the value does not give any clue to the stability at large angles of heel which is of prime importance in any boat. It is thus far better to consider the curve of righting levers and forget about metacentric height.

Open cockpits

Most motor cruisers have an open cockpit which means that when a certain angle of heel is reached water will pour into the cockpit. If a large quantity of water comes aboard this is the finale and the boat will either capsize or be swamped. This is the practical end point of the righting lever curve and is dictated mainly by the height of the gunwale above the normal waterline—the freeboard. The curve is stopped short by the presence of an open cockpit. The open cockpit is a positive limitation on the seaworthiness of a motor cruiser—it is a weak point and this fact must be borne in mind by the skipper under broaching conditions or when contemplating going to sea in rough conditions. The possibility of capsizing or being swamped by a wave crashing over the gunwale into the cockpit becomes greater the smaller the boat and the steeper and larger the waves. From this point of view conditions in the entrance to a harbour or river when tide and wind are running against each other can be just as dangerous as a wind of Force 7 or 8 well offshore. It is prudent never to run broadside-on to steep waves if the rolling becomes alarming. It is better to zig-zag. The position broadside-on presents the greatest danger of sudden capsize or swamping.

In most cruisers the limiting angle will not be small but something around 50° or 55° of heel. When a boat rolls heavily it is very easy to overestimate the actual angle of heel. 20° is quite frightening while 45° results in a shambles of arms and legs and crockery, so 50° or 55° in fact leaves quite a margin. In smaller cruisers there is no alternative to a cockpit, but a high freeboard, wide side decks and a high cockpit coaming will increase the angle at which water will start to come aboard (Figure 63). A self-draining cockpit is no real answer

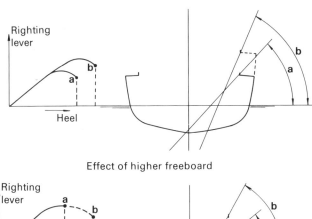

Effect of higher freeboard

Effect of wide sidedecks and high coamings

63   Cockpit flooding

because water may still flood the cockpit and add weight to the low side of the boat—even the largest-sized drain could not cope quickly enough. On the other hand to be self-draining, the sole of the cockpit has to be set above the normal waterline and is thus usually much smaller in floodable volume than a cockpit formed by the hull itself. The cockpit of a sea-going cruiser should be small and the boat should be equipped with a powerful bilge pump and several plastic buckets.

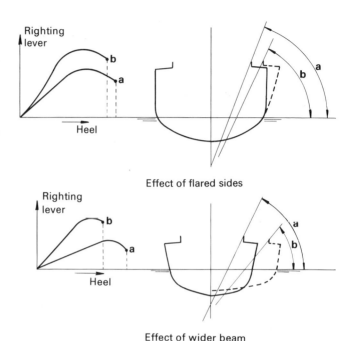

Effect of flared sides

Effect of wider beam

64   Stability effects

The chances of a boat rolling to such large angles are lessened if the craft is very stable up to the flooding-in angle. Flare on the sides of the boat (in its middle portion) will make the centre of buoyancy shift faster than will more vertical sides, while freeboard will extend the flooding-in point on the curve in Figure 64. Extra beam will increase the overall stability but, if the freeboard is not also increased, the angle of heel at which water will flood over the gunwale will be reduced. On the other hand, the greater breadth of the hull will create a larger righting moment, so the chances of the boat being rolled to such a large angle are less.

Centre of gravity

One other very important influence on the strength of the resistance to heeling is the position of the centre of gravity of the boat. The higher the position of the CG the less the horizontal separation between the CB and CG (the righting lever). Cruisers with large high cabins will have a high CG. On smaller sea-going craft headroom must be sacrified to keep the cabin height down. A high cabin will also catch the wind, increasing the heeling effect besides making steering difficult. Unfortunately, there are many small cruisers which not only have large cabins with full headroom but are also outboard-powered (the engine weight being at gunwale level) and un-ballasted, resulting in stability insufficient for seawork, though on sheltered waters they are quite safe.

The best sea-going cruiser has good freeboard for the beam and a low cabin profile above the gunwale. Associated with wide sidedecks and a high cockpit coaming this ensures that the angle of in-flooding is large while the windage presented by the cabin is low. To check on a particular cruiser it is best to compare her profile with other types of cruisers of about the same length. As a guide the freeboard at the lowest point should be more than 25 per cent of the overall breadth but not more than 35 per cent.

A sea-going boat must also have a low centre of gravity. Apart from the deleterious effect of high cabins mentioned so far there are a number of other points to consider. A heavy inboard diesel will entail a lower CG than an outdrive or an outboard. The general thicknesses of the structure should decrease the higher the position in the boat. A balsa-cored cabin top is a good weight saver while the chain locker should be sited as low as possible. Batteries and fuel tanks should also be sited as low as possible. It is the combination of all the items comprising the boat that dictate where the final CG lies. Once the boat is built there is not much scope for lowering the CG by moving only the batteries or chain locker, for example—the best way is to add ballast. To be effective the ballast added must be placed as far below the original CG as possible.

Sailing yachts require great stability in order to stand-up to the press of the wind on the sails. This is achieved with ballast equal in weight to a quarter or a half of the all-up weight of the boat, positioned externally in a keel as low as possible. Consequently yachts are generally self-righting assuming water cannot get inside the boat when upside down. Yacht cockpits are usually small and self-draining and the great leverage effect of the keel overcomes the loss of stability that a flooded cockpit entails. Even if a motor cruiser does not have an open cockpit, unballasted she will certainly not be self-righting but will probably capsize at around 90° of heel. So a motor cruiser is inherently less seaworthy than a sailing yacht.

The addition of ballast on a motor cruiser, however, does help. It lowers the CG and gives better righting levers, but the ballast must be fixed as low down as possible. Ideally this implies outside ballast, for example in the form of a cast iron bar attached to the underside of the keel. It must represent at least 5 per cent of the weight of the boat to make a significant improvement. Internal ballast in the bilges is less effective although still worthwhile. For instance the CG of a 26 ft motor cruiser may be 2 ft 6 in above the bottom edge of the keel. The keel may be 6 in deep and if the cast iron ballast blocks are 3 in thick then the CG of the ballast will only be 1 ft 10½ in below the original CG of the boat. If ballast equal to 5 per cent of the weight of the boat is added, the CG of the boat will be shifted downwards by $\frac{1}{20}$th of the 1 ft 10½ in dimension— a matter of only an inch. If the ballast is added twice as far away from the original CG it will have twice the effect. Internal ballast blocks must be secured in place in a sea-going boat and not merely laid in the bilge. If it did start to fall around the consequences could be disastrous.

An iron, steel or lead keel will greatly benefit the stability of a displacement cruiser. A deep wooden keel has the opposite effect. The buoyancy of the wood will tend to tip the boat upside down but, because the wooden keel will only displace a very small amount of water compared with the rest of the hull, the magnitude of the upsetting moment is small. A deep wood keel or bilge keels help to damp out rolling in a seaway and this is their intended purpose—they do not increase stability.

Planing cruisers cannot have ballast or deep keels. However a planing boat can be made more stable when off the plane by a hollow keel or low-down tank which automatically floods at low speeds and drains out at higher speeds. A floodable keel gives a worthwhile increase in righting levers at larger angles and a stiffer boat when at rest in calm water. This is particularly important for the deep vee type of hull.

Stability at rest

The tippiness at rest becomes important on cruisers of less than about 20 ft in length. This sort of stability depends mainly on the width of the hull at the waterline. If a boat is heeled very slightly, a cross section at the waterline (Figure 65) will show that a triangular wedge is pressed into the water on one side of the boat and a similar triangular wedge is lifted out of the water on the other. These two wedges constitute the

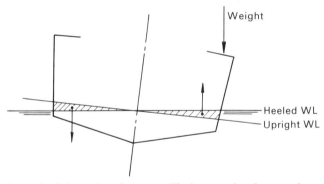

65   A boat heeled over in calm water. The immersed and emerged wedges resist the heeling force

resistance of the boat to heeling (the shift of buoyancy from one side to the other within the wedges causes the shift in CB) (see Figure 62). Clearly the greater the breadth of the boat the greater the area of the wedges and also the greater their leverage from the centre line. In fact the effects multiply together producing a cube effect: if the beam is doubled, the stiffness is increased eight-fold. In practice an extra foot of beam on an 18 ft by 6 ft boat will increase the stiffness by anything from 50 per cent to 100 per cent. A cruiser which continually shifts underfoot and heels excessively if two people happen to be on the same side may be dangerous for sea-work. Even on inland waters it takes some getting used to and does frighten people unaccustomed to boats.

Referring back to the wedges (Figure 65), the stiffness of a boat is dictated by the summation of the leverage effect of wedges all the way along the length of the hull. This means that features such as pointed sterns and cut-away bows diminish potential stiffness. The ideal waterplane shape from the stiffness point of view is a rectangle, which is closely approached by canal cruisers that are restricted in breadth and make the most of a given length by adopting a box-shaped hull.

Light shallow-draft cruisers such as those with shallow vee hard-chine hulls are generally very stiff when one moves around on board. But because of the lack of depth and grip in the water they give a feeling of sliding sideways from under one's feet, rather like rubber dinghies though not to such a great extent. This can only be cured by ballast to increase the weight and inertia of the boat, or by adding a long, deep keel to grip the water. This is another reason why a keel on such a craft is essential, providing that the boat is not required for planing speeds.

Buoyancy

If a timber-hulled motor cruiser fills with water she *may* still float—the natural buoyancy of the wood counteracts the denser-than-water items such as the engine. A steel, aluminium, concrete or GRP cruiser will definitely sink unless additional buoyancy is built into the boat. Dinghies are very often provided with ample buoyancy in the form of glassed-in hollow compartments, foam-filled cavities or air-filled bags. Only small GRP cruisers are normally fitted with built-in buoyancy. The larger the boat the less chance there is of being swamped in the first place and the greater the intrusion the required amount of buoyancy makes into the cabin space. Buoyancy must never be provided for solely in the bilges, which is unfortunate because here is waste space. Low-down buoyancy will tend to capsize the boat in the event of swamping.

The buoyancy should be provided along both sides of the boat under the gunwale, thus providing righting leverage when the boat is swamped. The submerged weight of the boat will be hanging on to the added buoyancy on each side. The buoyancy materials must be strongly held in place. It is a fairly simple matter to create foamed-in buoyancy spaces in a GRP cruiser and there are several examples of such unsinkable cruisers of 16–20 ft in length.

On larger craft, providing sufficient buoyancy becomes more difficult because of the amount required. Consider a 24 ft GRP cruiser—sunk. The buoyancy force needed to bring it to the surface is equal to the weight of the boat completely submerged. For instance, if a piece of GRP in air weighs 1 lb, in water it will only weigh $\frac{1}{3}$ lb. Similarly 1 lb of steel weighs $\frac{7}{8}$ lb in water, whereas 1 lb of timber gives a buoyancy of about 0·8 lb. One can total the weights of the individual materials in a typical inboard-engined 24 ft GRP cruiser and convert to a submerged weight. Thus such a cruiser weighing perhaps 2 tons in air will weigh about half a ton submerged in water. Half a ton of buoyancy will only just bring the boat up until the cabin top is at the surface of the water, and clearly to be useful the buoyancy must be able to lift the hull until the gunwales are above water. The superstructure and deck and all the fittings attached may weigh 600 lb or so in air, which means about 1700 lb of buoyancy in total is required, i.e. 1700 lb of water must be displaced. This is equal to about 27 cu ft and entails a watertight chamber of $13\frac{1}{2}$ cu ft on each side—say 16 ft long, 2 ft deep and 5 in wide. In practice, by fitting the bare minimum of buoyancy like this the builder would have to be careful to ensure that the buoyancy compartments are evenly spaced all along the length of the swamped waterline, otherwise the boat would be unstable, either rolling over sideways or ending up with the bows or stern pointing up in the air. The buoyancy should also cater for the crew clinging on and eventually crawling onto the cabin top, so in practice the minimum buoyancy needs to be doubled to be safe and one can see that the amount of space taken up is large.

As mentioned earlier not many cruisers over 20 ft in length are fitted with sufficient buoyancy to cater for swamping. One can argue that the space and money devoted to fitting buoyancy would be better used on items to reduce the chance of swamping ever occurring, such as a stout canvas storm cover for fitting over the cockpit when necessary, wide sidedecks and high coamings, and ballast. A powerful bilge pump and a sea anchor (for times of engine failure) are also items of importance.

The other method of preventing a boat sinking if the cockpit is flooded or if the boat is holed is to split the boat into several watertight compartments with watertight bulkheads. The top of each bulkhead has to be well above the normal outside waterline to allow for sinkage when one compartment is flooded. Clearly this method can only be applied to larger craft 30 ft and upwards in length. Watertight compartments only at each end of the boat may give sufficient buoyancy to keep the boat afloat but stability is unlikely to be positive and the boat will probably end up on her beam ends.

10 Steering and Handling

A properly designed cruiser should steer a straight course with infrequent helm correction, turn quickly when required and steer astern predictably. She should also have a grip on the water and not skitter sideways in a strong beam wind. Many cruisers on the market do not have these virtues. The shallow vee, hard-chine craft with only a rubbing strake type of keel invariably refuses to steer a straight course and in a strong wind is a veritable pig to handle. On the other hand, this type of boat has great responsiveness when it comes to turning sharply. A traditional style of displacement cruiser lies deep in the water and has a long keel considerably deeper at the after end, and a large rudder. In consequence a boat like this has the virtue of steering a straight course regardless of wind and waves with the minimum of wheel movement, but the radius of the turning circle is comparatively large. Also, steering astern is completely unpredictable—whichever way the wheel is put the boat chooses her own path.

Directional stability

The first type of boat mentioned is directionally unstable, while traditional displacement cruisers are directionally stable. An object which traverses a fluid can either travel in a smooth, straight line or flutter like a leaf falling to the ground. As an analogy consider an ordinary dart. The inertia of the brass weight together with the air drag on the feathers tends to keep the dart absolutely in line with its direction of motion (Figure 66). It is directionally stable—even if it is deflected off course for some reason it will rapidly steady up and carry on in a straight line. Thrown backwards a dart exhibits extreme

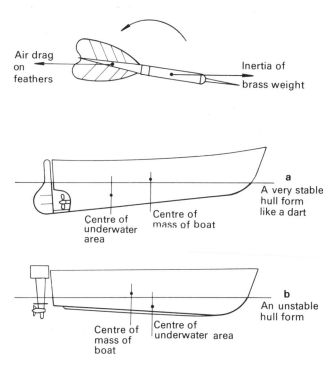

Air drag
on
feathers

Inertia of
brass weight

a
A very stable
hull form
like a dart

Centre of
underwater
area

Centre of
mass of boat

b
An unstable
hull form

Centre of
mass of
boat

Centre of
underwater area

66   Directional stability

directional *instability*—it immediately flicks around and flies the right way.

A boat with the extreme directional stability of a dart would be very difficult to turn and impossible to steer astern, but a small degree of stability makes steering very easy and pleasant. One should be able to leave the wheel for several minutes on a calm day without the boat going appreciably off course. Directional instability is caused by a lack of lateral underwater area aft (the feathers on a dart) whether inboard or outboard powered. The symptoms are very clear—in calm water the boat tends to wander off course, necessitating turning the wheel to counter the swing. The boat swings around, the wheel is centred, the boat then continues to swing, the wheel has to be turned the other way to stop the swing—and so on. The result is a zig-zag wake which is very pronounced if the helmsman is inattentive.

This phenomenon will be evident on a trial run of the chosen boat. If the boat is obviously unstable the builder or agent can be tackled, but often the reply is simply, 'She's better going faster'. This implies a certain lack of technical understanding of the problem, and also that she will be worse going slower. Apart from the problem of steering at cruising speed it is at slower speeds—coming alongside for example—that directional stability is important.

For non-planing boats the simple answer, a keel, should be provided at the design stage or at least before the boat is sold. The keel should taper deeper as it goes aft and stop about a quarter of the length of the boat forward of the transom. A long, straight keel will not necessarily do the trick—it needs to be deeper at the aft end to produce the dart effect. A large rudder or a plate rudder bolted to the outboard or outdrive will also help, in the sense that lateral area is being added at the after end. On the other hand, the steering will then be very sensitive in that the smallest wheel movement will produce a large steering effect. A keel is better and will also help to give a grip in the water to resist beam winds.

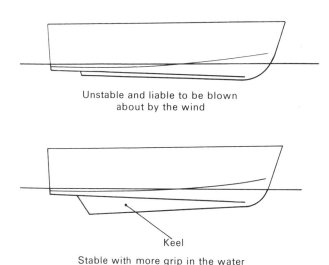

Unstable and liable to be blown
about by the wind

Keel

Stable with more grip in the water

67   Shallow vee hard-chine cruisers should have a deep keel if powered for lower speeds

In practice a 20 ft light, hard-chine, shallow vee cruiser should have a centre keel becoming deeper as it goes aft, stopping about 4 ft forward of the transom. If the boat is powered for speeds up to about 10 knots the keel can be quite deep—12–18 in at its after end (Figure 67). This should be the case whether outboard or outdrive powered. An inboard powered cruiser usually has a keel deep enough to protect the propeller in any case, thus giving inherent directional stability. In some inboard powered cruisers, however, the propeller shaft is supported by an A or P bracket and the keel is stopped short, giving insufficient lateral area aft.

For displacement craft rudders must not be too small. The drag they cause only becomes significant at planing speeds. When manoeuvring at slow speeds rudders which are too small give a vague response, especially when the propeller is not turning. The traditional hull form such as that of clinker boats usually has too much directional stability. The dead-wood (area of keel forward of the propeller) needs to be cut away (Figure 66a) or steering astern will be impossible and the turning circle rather large.

The drag of a large keel or a large rudder cannot be tolerated at planing speeds, so one may have to accept directional instability when a planing boat is proceeding slowly. Such a boat, when planing or when running at around the hump speed (with a pronounced bows-up attitude), will be directionally stable. Naturally when planing, trimmed to an angle of 4° or 6°, the centre of the underwater lateral area is well aft. Shallow vee hulls often exhibit this split personality; deeper vee hulls are usually stable throughout the speed range because the transom at the centreline is so deeply immersed. The apex of the bottom acts like the tail feathers of the dart.

Rudders and steering gear

There is not a lot to say about the rudder itself. Its shape is not important although a deep, narrow blade is theoretically more efficient than a long, shallow one. A square shape is most practical. Rudders which appear to be too small will probably give vague steering at low speeds. With displacement boats it is difficult to fit one too large. Ideally the rudder should be an aerofoil section, i.e. with a rounded leading edge and feathered trailing edge, but this feature is unimportant with displacement boats. What is more important is that the rudder is not too blunt and square-ended if it is made of wood, as this will cause unnecessary drag. An important practical point is that where possible, a keel bar should extend under the propeller and link up with the rudder (Figure 66a). This reduces the chance of a rope being caught by the rudder blade or wrapping round the propeller. A final point is that the rudder pintles (on a transom-hung rudder) or the bearings should be robust.

Most cruisers have wheel steering, but tiller steering is better in many ways for smaller craft where one can see easily over the cabin top. One feels more in command standing right aft with a tiller, where one can see what the whole length of boat is doing. Most people say that tiller steering is best for the heavy traditional canal cruiser.

Cable and pulley wheel steering is rarely fitted nowadays, the push-pull cable being almost universal. Morse and Tele-flex cables are commonly fitted and give a light lash-free positive control. However, with some steering mechanisms the water force on the rudder is not transmitted back to the steering wheel—there is no feel to the helm. This means that one cannot tell how much helm has been put on and, unlike a car steering wheel, when the wheel is let go it does not centre itself. This is usually true of outboard and outdrives where there is no large force to be transmitted back. The answer is to fit a rudder indicator on the steering console or, more simply, to mark one spoke of the wheel to indicate the mid-ships spoke.

Leeway

The greater the proportion of the boat above the waterline the more it will catch the wind and make handling at low speeds difficult. High topsides may enable full headroom to be achieved but one of the disadvantages is that the high sides will catch the wind. The types of cruiser most likely to be troublesome from windage are those with shallow draft (such as the shallow vee hard-chine hull) and those with a high profile forward. The first type will tend to skitter sideways in a strong wind and generally be blown all over the place, but the drawbacks of the latter require some explanation. Imagine a cruiser running along with a strong wind on the beam. If the above-water lateral area is concentrated forward the bows will be blown downwind and, to counteract this, the rudder will have to be held at a small angle (Figure 68). The boat will then

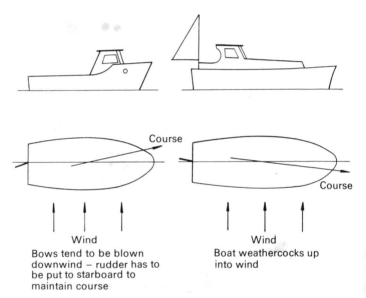

Bows tend to be blown
downwind – rudder has to
be put to starboard to
maintain course

Boat weathercocks up
into wind

68   Weathercocking effects

crab sideways and make leeway. The sketch shows the worst example of this type of boat—with a forward wheelhouse and raised forecastle. When manoeuvring, the tendency for the bows to be blown downwind makes life difficult because the rudder is at the other end of the boat. To make the bows point upwind the stern of the boat has to be kicked *downwind* by putting the rudder over to windward and engaging ahead, which will make matters worse if, for example, one is drifting onto the other side of the lock.

The other extreme profile drawn shows a boat which tends to weathercock bows into the wind. A mizzen sail will tend to make a boat do this. To maintain a steady course with a beam wind the rudder has to be put the opposite way. When manoeuvring, the weathercocking tendency is a great help. In practice neither of these two boats will drift (with the engine stopped) bows up, or stern up, into the wind—they will probably be no more than 45° to the wind. Which way the boat weathercocks is less important than the draft and grip of the hull in the water and the windage of the hull and cabin.

Handling

The traditional displacement inboard cruiser with its deep hull and grip on the water and large rudder is the easiest craft to handle. Manoeuvres can be done slowly and steering will be effective at slow speeds even if the propeller is stopped. The large rudder ensures this. When coming alongside the engine can be put into neutral and the boat steered with the rudder, until astern is selected. As the boat comes to a halt with the propeller turning astern, the flow of water over the rudder is completely disrupted and the steering is ineffective. The stern will be swung to one side which has to be taken into account when coming alongside. This swing is often called the paddle-wheel effect. A right-handed propeller (rotates clockwise in ahead when viewed from astern) will paddle the stern to port when astern is engaged. A left-handed propeller will do the opposite. Consequently it is easier to come alongside, port side to, with a boat with a right-handed propeller because the stern will be neatly swung into the jetty or lock when astern is engaged. Similarly when turning in a narrow river it is easier to do a three point turn starting off on the left-hand bank with the helm hard to starboard. When astern is engaged just before hitting the right-hand bank the right-handed propeller will tend to paddle the stern so that the boat swings in the desired direction. Some boats exhibit this tendency more than others. A large propeller and a large amount of deadwood enhance the effect, while it is not noticeable on boats with an outdrive or outboard.

A boat with an outdrive requires a different method of handling. With the propeller stopped there is no steerage: one has to use the propeller to produce a steering force. The direction of the force will depend on the steering wheel position and it is useful to have a rudder indicator by the wheel to show how the outdrive leg lies. Coming alongside, for instance, demands a bolder approach, continuously in gear, bearing in mind that the stern has to be swung to the required side by appropriate helm and throttle. At the last stage when the bows are in position but the stern is still some way out and the boat is still moving forward, a burst of astern power with the helm hard over *into* the jetty will both stop the boat and pull in the stern. Because of this power steering, outdrive cruisers steer astern quite well.

A twin-screw boat can be made to turn round in its own length by putting one engine ahead and the other astern. Together with single-lever controls, such a boat can be manoeuvred in a nimble and impressive way. In fact the steering wheel can be left amidships while manoeuvring. The manoeuvrability given by twin screws is a relatively minor advantage compared with the extra reliability and safety which two separate engines give at sea.

The remarks about outdrives also apply to outboards. The steering effect in neutral is non-existent. Light shallow drafted cruisers are usually associated with outboards, and on a windy day manoeuvring at slow speed can be very difficult. The approach must be made in a bold fashion which takes a little practice. The resistance to leeway is poor and so, with a strong beam wind, the boat will go along crab-wise. The leeway becomes greater the slower the speed, and has to be allowed for, for instance when entering a lock. Again a fast, bold approach is necessary. A deep keel is the solution to this problem while a plate rudder attached to the outboard leg also helps.

Steering a fast cruiser in calm water is a delightful experience. As mentioned before, directional stability is inherent, while turning is usually extraordinarily impressive. Deeper vee cruisers bank steeply *into* the turn like an aeroplane and one is pressed down into the seat with the centrifugal force.

There is always the possibility with fast planing boats of capsizing when turning very tightly at high speeds. Shallow vee hulls are rather more liable to capsize than deeper veed craft. If the boat heels outwards from the turn then there is something seriously wrong. A capsize can be caused by the chine on the outside of the turn digging in and tripping the boat over sideways. A deep vee hull banks into the turn more than a shallow vee hull, and in any case the chines run higher. On a modern moderate or deep vee cruiser one can turn the wheel harder and harder and all that happens is that the boat turns tighter and tighter until the speed drops so much that she falls off the plane. A shallow vee hull makes more leeway in a turn, as if she were on ice, and does not bank so much into the turn.

Extreme deep vee hulls sometimes exhibit other frightening tendencies. A common one is the sudden flopping-over onto one side of the bottom and consequent running along with a pronounced list. This can be due to several causes—a strong wind on the beam, too many people on one side of the boat or, more fundamentally, an instability in the flow over the bottom of the boat. Deep vee hulls are apt to be tender when running fast as well as when stationary, simply because the portion of hull in the water is narrow. Despite this lesser initial stability they are safe in the sense that as the boat heels over, more and more righting buoyancy is picked up by the vee bottom and flared sides.

Cavitation is often noticeable in a tight turn—the engine races and vibrates and thrust is lost. If it occurs in quite moderate turns, badly reducing the speed of the boat, something is seriously wrong. It is usually caused by the propeller suddenly finding itself being fed with water shedding off the end of the keel or some other obstruction which only affects the water flowing to the propeller in a turn. Outboards and outdrives are at an advantage here because the water flow is always in line with the propeller, in contrast to an inboard arrangement where, in a turn, the propeller will be going through the water diagonally.

From the point of view of broaching, outdrives and outboards have some advantage over the inboard. Inboard-powered planing cruisers necessarily have small rudders which become ineffective when the craft is forced to slow down under broaching conditions. The outboard or outdrive with 'power steering' will give a greater response when the helmsman, feeling the stern beginning to swing, quickly puts the wheel over and opens the throttle.

The steering position

Vision from the steering position is particularly important. The helmsman must be able to see the water three boat lengths ahead and preferably as close as one boat's length ahead. Bear in mind that under way, the bows will lift, especially with a planing boat when climbing onto the plane. Naturally one should also be able to see sideways and it is preferable to be able to see astern without having to leave the wheel. It is only in a cruiser with a forward cockpit or wheelhouse where this view may be restricted.

Quite often vision is good when standing but poor when seated. This is a simple matter of the seat being fitted at the wrong height. Similarly the ergonomics of the sitting position are often poor, the wheel spokes fouling the legs so that the helmsman has to sit side-saddle or with legs wide apart. This is usually because the wheel is mounted on a vertical bulkhead whereas it should be inclined to the vertical like the steering wheel of a car (Figure 69). A foot rest is often missing so that one's legs dangle. It is difficult to combine comfort when seated with room to stand at the wheel when required. Some compromise is necessary but good vision forward is of first importance.

Outboards, outdrives, and inboard engines with hydraulic gearboxes allow single lever engine/gear controls to be mounted alongside the wheel, which is ideal. A gear lever protruding through the floorboards just aft of the engine box may require the helmsman to step back and bend down briefly to select ahead or astern.

If the helmsman has to look through a windscreen, glass is much superior to Perspex because the latter scratches and becomes opaque after a few seasons. A windscreen wiper will

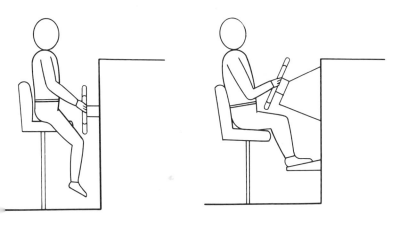

69   Uncomfortable and comfortable steering positions

quickly score a Perspex window, especially at sea where salt deposits may dry on the screen. If the windscreen is sloped aft too much, vision is impaired. A white reflective cabin top immediately in front of the helmsman is trying on the eyes on a sunny day—darker colours are better.

Working the boat

When choosing a cruiser it pays to imagine how easy it will be to anchor or tie-up, not from the helmsman's point of view but for the crew. Easy access to the foredeck is a prime requirement. Is it easy to step up out of the cockpit and onto the sidedeck? A step just below gunwale level makes this a lot easier. Once up on the sidedeck, ease and safety of walking forward depend on the width of the deck, the non-slip property of the surface and whether grab-rails come readily to hand (Figure 70). Stanchions and guard rails are ideal but only really possible on boats over about 22 ft in length. The moulded-in tread pattern seen on some GRP boats is by no means anti-slip—the best surface is a non-slip paint (paint with fine grit added) or a covering such as Trakmark or 'sandpaper' tread strips. A toe-rail adds to security, but on a wooden boat may

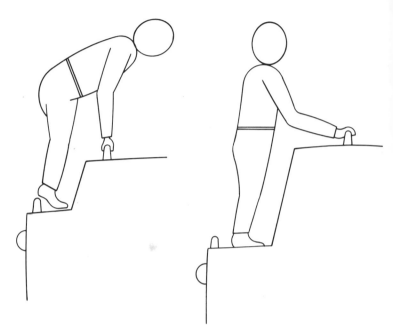

70   Good and bad sidedecks

be the first place where rot will appear. A pulpit is very necessary on the foredeck for sea-going boats so that the crew have
something to hang on to when the boat is pitching and rolling.
A raised fo'c'sle has the disadvantage that the person standing
up there is that much higher off the water, making it for
instance more difficult to pick up a buoy.

For sea-going boats an anchor and chain or warp should not
merely be stowed in the cockpit. The fittings necessary to
facilitate pulling up an anchor and stowing the chain are simple
and fairly cheap. A chain roller, a navel pipe, a chain locker
and deck chocks are needed (Figure 71). The chain roller
avoids the chain scraping inboard over the gunwale and allows
a horizontal fall. The weight of the chain pulls it through the
navel pipe to stow in a heap in the chain locker. A self-stowing
anchor arrangement is ideal, i.e. one where the anchor does
not have to be lifted inboard and stowed. With a GRP boat it
should be possible to arrange a moulded-in deck stowage for
the anchor. It is essential to fit an anchor and chain on sea-

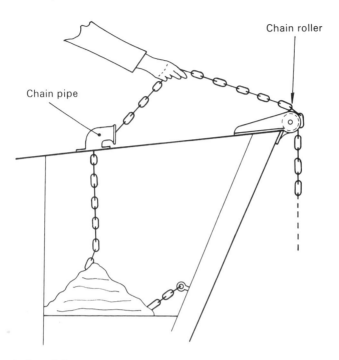

Chain roller

Chain pipe

71 Anchor chain arrangement

going boats, while on rivers being able to anchor will prevent the boat drifting towards a weir in the event of engine failure.

When coming alongside the usual practice is to employ separate fenders to prevent damage to the hull. They are effective for smooth walls or when alongside another boat, but useless if there are vertical piles. An all-round rubber fender (of generous size) at gunwale level is the best solution, although fenders will still be necessary on occasion. The plastic strip moulding which is fitted around the cabin/hull joint of some GRP cruisers is too thin to absorb much energy and, if not secured at close intervals, is liable to get caught and pulled off. Fenders will need to be stowed somewhere, probably in a locker in the cockpit, and when in use will require to be tied onto the grab rails or fender eyes. Check that fender eyes, if fitted, are not so positioned as to stub toes. Ropes will also need to be stowed when not in use.

Bollards and cleats are often too small for the job—especially on a sea-going cruiser where one might have to lie in a trot with other boats moored alongside on both sides. In this case there might be four or more lines to secure to the forward bollard and another four or more aft. Apart from the size of the bollard or cleat it is essential that it is bolted or screwed very securely in place. The forward bollard must be able to take the strain when the boat is towed and the continual snatch of a chain mooring on windy days. On GRP boats this means that through bolts must be used and a substantial pad of wood or increased thickness of GRP incorporated under the bollard fitting. Fairleads fitted at the gunwale will prevent ropes chafing the deck edge.

11   Inland Craft

Factors that influence the design of a cruiser for inland waters have been mentioned in nearly every chapter, but there are some specific points which have not been covered. A good canal cruiser is totally different to a sea-going heavy displacement or deep vee cruiser. Inland boats are different because the environment is different; so too are the people who like placid waters. Most people who have a boat on the sea would never dream of deliberately changing to the canals or a river. Similarly canal enthusiasts usually have no strong wish to take to the sea: the two scenes are totally different.

To cruise inland in a hurry and to aim to do as many miles as possible in a day is to lose the point of it all. One must accept an average speed of only a few miles an hour, while an hour's delay at a lock must be regarded with equanimity. Meals can be eaten while tied up to the bank. There are no tides to worry about, and one can usually park the car alongside the boat and step straight aboard without having to haul around and load up a dinghy. If there is a current it is usually of only a fraction of a knot in the summer. Seaworthiness is a matter of indifference and there will be no spray coming over the bows to wet the occupants of the cockpit. Even the wind is damped by the surrounding trees and bushes. Some waterways such as the Broads and the lower reaches of the upper Thames are becoming crowded, but there are some stretches of rivers and canals which are so utterly remote that one could not wish for more peace and quiet.

Hull shapes

Because speeds are low and the water calm, hull forms can be chosen to give the maximum amount of room inside and the greatest initial stability rather than bowing to the demands of the sea. For both these aspects a rectangular box-shaped hull is theoretically ideal, albeit with some pretence at a pointed bow to reduce the large resistance that a purely box-shaped hull would create. Cabins can be tall giving full headroom on a smaller boat. For a given length a lot can be packed into such a boat, but the result from an aesthetic point of view is rather dismal. Some people would willingly sacrifice some room inside in order to have a more boat-shaped craft, perhaps one primarily intended for the sea. So long as the draft and breadth are not too great there is no reason why a curvacious round-bilge cruiser should not be used inland. The Nelson 18 springs to mind as just such a boat.

A flat-bottomed box-shaped hull sits lightly on the water— the draft without ballast will be a matter of inches only. For instance a 22 ft cruiser fully fitted out including an engine will weigh perhaps $1\frac{1}{2}$ tons and, when floating, it must displace $1\frac{1}{2}$ tons of water which has a volume 54 cu ft. If the hull is 22 ft long and 7 ft wide it will displace 154 cu ft for every foot it is immersed. But it only needs to displace 54 cu ft so the draft will equalise at about $\frac{1}{3}$ ft or 4 in. The snag with a shallow-draft box hull is that it catches the wind very easily making handling difficult. To get a decent grip on the water a great deal of ballast will be required to force the boat down lower. A more boat-shaped hull with a round bottom and tapering bow and stern will naturally sit deeper in the water.

Most GRP cruisers one sees on inland waters have shallow vee hulls. They are virtually flat-bottomed boxes, but the manufacturers give them vee hulls, partly to give more draft and more grip and partly so that they can be offered as planing cruisers for the sea. As the reader will probably have gathered in other chapters the shallow vee hull makes a poor sea boat. Such cruisers also make poor boats for cruising inland because of the handling difficulty. The handling problem is more a matter of lack of keel than of poor hull shape because, as I said earlier, a hydrodynamically good hull shape is not a prime requirement. Because planing cruisers cannot have deep keels, these are not fitted to the builder's standard boat and so one sees keels of only a few inches depth, giving a total draft of little over a foot. Taken together with the windage of a large 6 ft headroom cabin the boat inevitably handles badly. If the keel does not taper deeper as it goes aft, the boat will also be directionally unstable and, in combination with an outboard motor, the overall result is confusion and embarrassment for the owner, and amusement for onlookers watching from the lock side.

In the design of an inland cruiser there are two ways round the problem. Basically one needs draft, preferably for most of the length of the boat. This can be achieved either by adding ballast until the boat sinks to the required draft, or by fitting a single deep keel, again to give the right draft. The right draft is about 1 ft 9 in and 2 ft. On a shallow vee hull this would represent a keel about 12 in deep. It would still allow the boat to cruise all the shallow English canals. Traditional canal boats adopt the other method—ballast. Paving stone ballast is fitted in the bottom throughout the length of the boat and there has to be an awful lot of it because, as pointed out earlier, to force a box-shaped hull down in the water takes a great amount of weight over and above that of the boat herself.

The ubiquitous shallow vee GRP cruiser, nine times out of ten, has an aft cockpit. For inland use a forward cockpit is more logical because everyone aboard can more easily see the scenery and also be away from the noise of the engine. Perhaps it is once again a question of builders building boats to be offered for use on the sea as well as the canals. Such boats usually have no sheer—the gunwale line runs forward in a flat and uninteresting way. Despite the fact that seaworthiness is no criterion, a smooth sweeping sheer is a delight to the eye and brings no disadvantages in its wake. Notably the traditional canal cruiser has sheer.

To continue on a critical theme, most GRP craft seen on rivers and canals have white hulls, often also with white superstructures and a blue canvas cover over the aft cockpit. The uniformity and monotony presented to the eye by lines of these cruisers at their moorings could so easily be broken. The traditional colours on the 'cut' are bright green and red, with hulls painted black, which may not be to everyone's taste but at least they add contrast.

A cruiser on inland waters has to come alongside frequently, so an all-round gunwale fender of substantial size is very useful. Fenders and fender eyes are still needed for securing the lines. Manoeuvrability is of importance and the draft in relation to the above-water windage has been discussed already. Outboards and outdrives give no steerage when the propeller is stopped and a plate rudder attached to the lower leg will help. Even if an inboard is fitted to a shallow vee cruiser, when the propeller is stopped the steerage can be vague, usually because the rudder fitted is too small. For slow speed work one cannot have too large a rudder.

To go too fast inland is to be antisocial in two ways: the wash erodes the banks and upsets other craft moored to the bank. Most waterways have legal speed limits in any case, but it is the skipper's responsibility to judge the size of his wash and whether it will do any harm. On relatively deep and wide rivers 6 knots can be achieved without causing too much commotion, but the shorter the boat the greater the wash and the more slowly one should go. As explained in Chapter 2 it is the speed:length ratio which determines the wash and as a rule speed should be restricted to give a speed:length ratio of 1 ($4\frac{1}{2}$ knots on a 20-footer; 5 knots on a 25-footer).

When the depth of water is restricted, as in a shallow canal, a boat may be held back to 2 or $2\frac{1}{2}$ knots by the sheer resistance of the water. If there is only a few inches under the bottom the water has to flow around the sides to fill the 'hole' behind the boat. This effect is very marked if the width of the canal is also restricted. One can see the water rushing aft with the weeds on the bottom bending back. The cross section of the boat represents a fair proportion of the cross section of the canal and the effect is rather like a piston being forced up a cylinder.

A sea cruiser is more often than not brought ashore for the winter and in any case the tides make it easy to beach the boat in order to paint the hull. Inland it is not so easy to maintain the underside, and a GRP hull is a more logical choice than timber by far. Timber rots more easily in fresh water and, if a hull is left afloat for several years without regular painting below the waterline, the wood is likely to become soft. A timber hull needs annual lifting out and repainting. Fresh water is not so corrosive to mild steel and this material is a good choice, especially on canals where scrapes and bumps are inevitable. Indeed the atmosphere inland is not so corrosive as a salt atmosphere and one finds that steel equipment including the engine does not rust nearly so quickly. Clothes and sleeping bags left on board stay dry longer.

Beware of outboard dealers advising an outboard which is too large for the boat (see Chapter 7). Providing the engine size chosen is sensible, any type will return a low fuel consumption though a small diesel will be best (see Chapter 8). A noisy engine on a calm summer's day is doubly irritating, so good insulation is worth while.

Equipping a boat for cruising inland is far less expensive than equipping a similar boat for the sea. The only safety gear which need be carried on board are a fire extinguisher, lifejackets and an anchor. Two fire extinguishers should be carried, one fitted close to the galley and one by the engine. Buoyancy aids are perhaps more practical in lieu of lifejackets for children and non-swimmers, and an anchor is only necessary where the waterway has weirs and is likely to become swollen after a very rainy period.

Narrow canals

To cruise all the navigable canals in England and Wales the beam must be less than 7 ft, the draft less than 2 ft and the height above water no more than 5 ft 4 in. Most canal craft have a beam of 6 ft 10 in to give an inch or two clearance in locks which are 7 ft wide. Canal bridges and tunnels are arched, so the cabin roof needs to be steeply cambered to suit. Length is no problem as most locks will take boats of 70 ft.

A boat intended to cruise the canals must expect to take knocks and scrapes in her stride and in this respect GRP is not the best material. Its abrasion resistance is poor and hulls must be protected with several full length rubbing strakes. In a narrow lock there may be no room for fenders and no matter how careful the owner is, mishaps occur. Locks are an inescapable part of inland cruising, and whereas the locks on rivers such as the Thames are large and well maintained, canal locks are usually small and narrow and unattended. The boat must be able to look after herself to some extent. She must be able to slide up and down inside the lock without catching on anything. This implies slab sides with preferably a tumble-home gunwale. Flare on the bows can be a nuisance. The traditional canal boat has an inward bent top to the stem so that it does not hook under lock gates.

The rubbish lying on the canal bottom is an unseen hazard waiting to add another scrape to the hull and to entangle the propeller. It is essential to be able to get to the propeller easily, which is a good reason to choose outboard or outdrive power. With an inboard installation a weed hatch is usually incor-porated. This is a hatch directly over the propeller having its coaming a few inches above the water level. Thus it is possible to reach down and clear the propeller. Weed is a menace not only to the propeller but to the water intake—hence the ad-vantage of an air-cooled engine. The disadvantage is the extra noise. Jet drives, if fitted with an intake grill, perform better than a propeller in weedy conditions, but their disadvantages for slow speed work tend to outweigh this advantage.

Traditional canal boats

The heavy ballasted traditional canal boat usually has a steel hull. This material is considered by most canal enthusiasts to be the best because of its robustness. Rusting is no great problem even without the use of exotic modern paints. Because the hull will be scraped so often a paint scheme which is easily touched-up is an advantage. Bituminous paint is often used in lieu of the traditional coating which has a mixture of tar, pitch and horse dung (from a corn-fed horse) brewed over a fire and slapped on hot! Plating is either $\frac{3}{16}$ in or $\frac{1}{4}$ in thick, fully welded with angle bar stiffeners across the bottom and up the sides. Half-round bar rubbing strakes are usually welded along the topsides. Both the top and bottom edges of these strakes should be welded. The standard of welding of the hull can be roughly judged by the appearance of the weld.

It should be neat and straight with no blow holes or slag deposits. Fuel and water tanks can be built-in to the hull and bulkheads can be welded at the forward end of the engine room to contain fuel and oil drips. Similarly gas bottle stowages can be built-in and vented overboard.

The cabin is usually made of plywood, steel or GRP. GRP is perhaps the best choice because it stands up to the weather better than plywood and does not require the painting which steel demands. The cabin should not take nearly so many knocks as the hull and does not need to be as strong.

The most popular type of engine for these boats is a slow-running 'thump-thump' diesel, air-cooled to avoid the weed problem. Only small engines of 10 to 20 h.p. are required even when the length approaches 70 ft. It is interesting to note that the power:weight ratio is extremely low—a 40 footer weighing about 10 tons may have an engine of 10 h.p. Compared with a fast planing boat which must have over 100 h.p. per ton, the traditional canal boat is exceedingly economical in power and fuel. Because of the great weight and low power, the handling of a traditional canal boat is delightfully slow and ponderous with strong winds having no effect—in direct contrast to the shallow vee outboard cruiser.

The large amount of ballast which has to be fitted to the traditional canal boat gives extreme initial stability, considering the narrow beam. The centre of gravity of the boat is very low and consequently these boats are quite safe on more exposed rivers.

Special equipment needed for canal cruising includes a lock windlass (and a spare), a spot light and a boarding plank—often the water is too shallow near the bank to get the boat right alongside.

12 Equipment

Unlike a new motor car, a new motor cruiser is rarely sold in all respects ready for sea. The builder's brochure may claim that a whole host of equipment is fitted as standard and the boat is ready bar cutlery and bedding. But all too often, even if the boat is to be used inland, fenders and ropes will be needed within the first mile, and on the sea the most basic equipment such as an anchor and chain may be missing from the inventory. Equipping a cruiser for inland waters is relatively simple and inexpensive; all the recommended gear for sea-work will add another hundred or even two hundred pounds to the cost of the boat.

To moor a boat one either needs ropes and fenders for an alongside mooring or a stem roller (preferably) in the case of a swinging mooring. If the boat is not accessible from land, a dinghy is a first essential. The cockpit should not be left un-covered so a cockpit canopy is required. When the season is over even a GRP cruiser will need an all-over winter cover—(Terylene cotton canvas—about 8 oz—is the best material).

For canal cruising a windlass handle for the locks and a searchlight for tunnels may be necessary. GRP and wooden craft need good protection with fitted rubbing strakes and fenders, but a steel cruiser will take the scrapes in its stride.

On rivers an anchor and chain or warp (rope) are advisable to cater for the occasions when the engine breaks down up-stream of a weir. (This occurrence is by no means rare—the Thames Conservancy recommend you carry an anchor.) A horn is useful to warn other people who have not heard you coming and a boat hook is a necessity on *any* boat (an arm is often not long enough). For locks, ropes forward and aft need to be long enough to reach up and around the lock posts and

back down to the boat. 20 ft is the least length, but of course
it depends on the depth of the lock.

The following list of safety gear should be carried by sea-
going motor cruisers used within three miles of land. It is
basically that recommended by the Department of Trade and
Industry in their publication *Safety on Small Craft* (HMSO)
which incidentally is a very readable booklet.

Lifejackets	One for each person on board.
Lifebuoys	Two (one with self-igniting light if night sailing).
Fire extinguishers	Minimum is one 3 lb unit (for the engine) but if a cooker is fitted an additional one should be sited near the cooker.
Buckets	Two with lanyards (ropes) attached for fire fighting.
Anchors	Two, with chains or warps.
Bilge pump	One.
Compass	One, plus a small spare.
Charts	One for the appropriate area, plus tide tables and tidal atlas.
Flares	Six (red) with two of the rocket/parachute type.
Smoke	Daylight distress signals (orange).
Tow rope	This needs to be a good length to reduce 'snatch' (say 100 ft).
First aid box	Including anti-seasickness pills.
Radio receiver	Ordinary portable radio for weather forecasts.
Torch	Water resistant.
Radar reflector	As large as possible.
Lifeline	Line to be used as inboard lifeline in bad weather when on deck in conjunction with one or more safety harness.
Tool kit	Including engine spares.
Name	In letters at least 9 inches high.

Most of the items in the list are self-explanatory, but there
are some qualifying comments. On the subject of personal

buoyancy there are two distinct types of garment—lifejackets and buoyancy aids. Proper lifejackets—preferably to BS 3595—are rather bulky to wear continuously, but have a great deal of buoyancy. They should be worn if conditions become dangerous.

Buoyancy aids are comfortable to wear continuously but have much less buoyancy. They are only suitable for use when the person is not to be in the water for very long and where help is close by. For non-swimmers or for occasions when there is a distinct chance of falling overboard a buoyancy aid is the answer. They should be to the standard of the Ship and Boat Builders' National Federation.

Lifebuoys have two functions—as personal buoyancy in the event of the boat sinking and as something to sling to a man overboard. Obviously lifebuoys must not be tied to the boat in any way, but either held in a tray or secured with elastic cords and positioned within reach of the helmsman. The 30 in diameter lifebuoy is preferable to any smaller imitations.

Fire extinguishers nowadays usually contain either dry powder or BCF. BCF is clean and effective but the fumes can be harmful in a confined space. CO_2 or foam extinguishers are acceptable alternatives.

An anchor and a chain are basic items in the inventory of a sea-going boat. There are many types of anchor but the three most usual are the fisherman, the plough and a modern type of patent anchor such as the Meon. The latter two give more holding power in most types of bottom than the fisherman and are easier to stow. Choosing an appropriate size of anchor (in terms of weight) is difficult because it depends on how much windage the boat has, whether chain or a nylon warp is used and how much is paid out. As a rough guide, a 16 ft cruiser should have a modern-type 10 lb anchor, a 20-footer a 15 lb and a 30-footer a 30 lb anchor. The holding power depends on how horizontal the pull is on the anchor itself so chain is really better than a nylon warp, but of course costs more, and in a fast boat represents more weight to carry around. If a warp is used (nylon rope is best as it has great elasticity to absorb snatch), a length of chain—about 20 ft—should be shackled on the anchor with the remaining length made up of nylon. One must guard against chafe, for instance where the nylon passes through a fairlead. Except in calm, tideless water far more chain or warp has to be let out than that necessary for the anchor to touch bottom. In fact there are few occasions when less than four times the depth of water gives safe anchoring. Consequently 50 ft of chain is of little use and 100 ft is the bare minimum.

When a compass is bought and fitted in a boat allowance must be made for the fact that it will not read correctly. Apart from variation (which is the difference between magnetic North and true North) there is deviation (which is caused by all the metal fittings on the boat). Deviation can be made very small by carefully siting the compass away from items made of steel or iron or cables carrying electric current. It is the proximity of metal to the compass that counts: 3 or 4 ft is sufficient clearance even from a bulky engine. Objects containing steel or iron should never subsequently be placed near the compass—metal framed spectacles, wrist watches, etc.

Resinglass happens to be transparent to radar waves and wood is not much better. In any case a small boat represents a tiny low-down object for the radar set on a ship to pick up. Thus a radar reflector is a great comfort especially in misty or foggy weather in shipping channels. A radar reflector is merely a set of metal plates arranged in three planes. It should be at least 10 ft above the sea.

The most useful tools to carry are a screwdriver, a pair of pliers, an adjustable spanner and several assorted double-ended spanners. Bits and pieces such as lengths of plastic tube, wire, electric cable, nails and screws can be useful. For inboards a spare water pump impellor and water pump belt should be carried, together with a contact breaker set and spare sparking plugs. For outboards a few shear pins and spare sparking plugs are advisable and, whatever the engine, the manufacturer's handbook should be on board, and a can of spare fuel. Ideally spare injectors and a spare fuel filter element should be carried on a diesel-engined cruiser. At least the skipper should be familiar with the fuel system and the sequence of bleeding.

The name of your boat should be in large letters, preferably on each side amidships, perhaps on the aft end of the cabin sides. This makes the work of the Coastguard easier if you take advantage of their free service for surveillance on coastal passages. In the ultimate it makes the work of rescuers easier and in crowded harbours is a blessing to such people as Harbourmasters.

For cruisers going more than 3 miles offshore it is recommended that an inflatable liferaft should be carried. These are expensive and a dinghy with permanent buoyancy or an inflatable dinghy kept inflated are alternatives. The dinghy or the inflatable should be carried on deck and have oars and rowlocks positively attached.

Other important items

As mentioned in Chapter 6 no engine is totally reliable and an alternative means of propulsion figures large in any list of safety equipment for motor cruisers. An emergency outboard is the obvious choice for smaller cruisers in which case a bracket is required on the transom, together with cans of spare fuel and an inboard stowage space. Without power a motor cruiser will lie broadside-on to wind and wave and will wallow and roll dangerously in a rough sea. Some means of making the boat lie partially stern-to or bow-to the waves will reduce the roll. In shallow water the obvious answer is to anchor. In deep water letting out the anchor and some chain will produce a drag effect on the bows tending to swing them upwind. A sea-anchor (which works like a parachute and is shaped like a short wind sock) will also give this effect, but it must be at least 2 ft in diameter to be of any use. Streaming the anchor or sea-anchor from the stern rather than the bow is usually more effective on motor cruisers.

Climbing aboard a boat from the water is usually impossible without assistance or a foothold situated just below the water with which to heave oneself up. The simple answer is a boarding ladder which when fitted in place extends down into the water. Apart from its use when bathing it is an important piece of gear for the occasion when someone falls overboard. The water may be rough and cold and the person fully clothed. It is easy to imagine the difficulty in hauling someone aboard in such conditions without a ladder.

If you intend to cruise after dark or if there is a chance of being caught out after dark at sea, navigation lights must be fitted. The familiar red (to port) and green (to starboard) side lights should shine from dead ahead to $22\frac{1}{2}°$ abaft the beam and be visible for 1 mile. According to the *International Regulations for Preventing Collisions at Sea* a white light should also be fitted shining forward to $22\frac{1}{2}°$ abaft the beam on each side and positioned at least 3 ft above the red and green lights. This light should be visible for 3 miles. An overtaking light should shine aft $67\frac{1}{2}°$ on either side from dead aft and be visible for 2 miles. The lights fitted to many cruisers do not comply with these regulations mainly on account of their lack of size and brightness. The miniature navigation lights normally encountered in yacht chandlers have bulbs of 6 or 10 watts, which is alright for inland waters, but at sea at least 20 watts is required. When anchored in a busy waterway at night an anchor light should be shown. It should be white and fitted forward and should shine all round. A fog horn should be carried and used according to the Regulations.

A great deal of rope is required for coastal cruising. One may have to moor between piles in a trot alongside several other boats with the possibility of more boats coming alongside your own. In such circumstances to attach all the mooring lines requires large bollards or cleats forward and aft and many cruisers are woefully lacking in this respect.

A boat hook is necessary wherever the boat is to cruise and a pulpit is useful. For coastal cruising and if the crew is to be asked to go forward, a pulpit is essential.

For the safety of the boat a battery master switch, a fuel tap (on a petrol-engined boat) and a seacock are desirable, and also an hour-meter to ensure proper servicing of the engine. More importantly one must know, or be able to find out, how much fuel remains in the tank especially on a sea-going boat. A fuel gauge is one way, a dipstick a more reliable way. If a gauge is not fitted the boat builder should provide a calibrated dipstick.

When considering what extra equipment to fit to a boat get the priorities right. At sea, safety for the family comes first, refrigerators and tooth brush holders come last. In the middle are such worthwhile extras as large ventilators, flexible engine mountings, noise insulation, a windscreen wiper and perhaps a cabin heater.

13 Some Motor Cruisers Assessed

The motor cruisers briefly assessed in the following pages are just a few of those on the market and have been chosen to illustrate all the different types available, the different hull forms and cabin/cockpit layouts. There is a dearth of some types of cruiser, in particular the fast round-bilge and heavy displacement varieties. There are any number of shallow vee cruisers devoted to giving as much accommodation as possible.

The figures given for displacement and draft can be compared with the comments in Chapter 3 and especially with Figure 24. The draft quoted for each motor cruiser is the distance below the waterline of the underside of the keel (if any) at its deepest part (usually aft), or the hull at its deepest part; outdrive or outboard legs are excluded. Thus the draft given is a measure of the grip in the water. The displacement given is for the boat with engine (except in the case of an outboard-powered boat) but excludes the weight of fuel and water. The waterline length is given so that the speed:length ratio may be worked out by the method explained in Chapter 2. The engine power can be used on Figures 53 to 55 and the probable fuel consumption can be worked out using Chapter 8. Comparison of the beam and above-water profile should be made with similar boats. The beam quoted is usually that at gunwale level excluding any rubbing fenders. The hull lay-up quoted can be checked with Figure 37. The prices given are only intended to give an indication of the price level of each boat as fitted with a reasonable amount of equipment. In the case of fast boats with different engine options a great range of price can be expected. VAT is included.

Shetland 536, around £750 excluding the outboard
Birchwood Continental, around £750 excluding the outboard

Marina 16, around £600 excluding the outboard
Microplus 501, around £700 excluding the outboard
Pacific 550, around £1000 excluding the outboard
Seaworker 22, £3500–£4000
Parker 24, £5000–£5500
Aquaboat Fisher, £4000–£4500
Versatility 25, £5000–£6000
Pearson 26, £4500–£5000
Sea Angler 31, £6000–£7000
Mitchell 23, hull and superstructure around £1300
Maclan 22, £5000–£6000
Dolphin 23, £4000–£5000
Norman 23, £2500–£3000 excluding the outboard
Freeman 23, £3500–£4000
Seamaster 23, £4500–£5500
Fjord Cruiser £8000–£10 000
Nimbus, £7000–£8000
Waterland 75, £6000–£7000
Fairline Fury, £7500–£9500
Cleopatra 850, £6000–£10 000
Kingswift, £8000–£11 000
Orrskar, £8000–£12 000
Senior 31, £9000–£11 000
Latham Sturgeon, £1750–£2000
Aqua Star 19, £2500–£3000
Atlanta, £3000–£3500
Ardleigh Laminated Plastics, Colvic 26·5, hull only around
    £1000; hull, deck and wheelhouse around £2000
Parkstone Bay, £3000–£3500
Dauntless 20, around £2500
Dauntless 24, £5000–£6000
Myra 21, £4000–£4500
Saga 20, £3500–£4500
Island Plastics 23, hull only around £600
Albin 25, £6000–£7000
Viksund 27, £6000–£7000
Hardy 8·25, hull and all other mouldings, bulkheads, hull
    stiffening and ballast around £4000
Drago 2000, £4000–£6000

Skagerak, £5000–£6000
Fjord 21, £5000–£7000
Triana 25, £10 000–£14 000
Fjord 30, £13 000–£15 000
Fairey Fantome, £20 000–£25 000
Apollo, £19 000–£23 000
Weymouth 32, £25 000–£30 000
Dawncraft 22, £1600–£1900 excluding the outboard
Burland 26, £3000–£4000
Dobson 24, £3500–£4500
Trentcraft, £2300–£2600 excluding the engine. Ready to fit
   out internally costs around £1800
Harborough Marine, 36 ft—£5000–£6000. 56 ft—£8000–
   £10 000

Small fast outboard-powered cruisers

Light-weight GRP mini-cruisers of 15 to 18 ft in length with
a hard chine hull and a small cabin are popular because they
are relatively cheap and easy to trail behind the family car.
They are designed to cruise gently along a canal with a
5 h.p. outboard, or tear around in unrestricted waters or
calm sea with a 40 or 60 h.p. outboard. The restriction
on beam caused by English canals does not make boats of
this length unduly narrow, so stability is not compromised
when they are used on more open waters. On the other hand I
would hesitate to recommend such small craft for offshore
cruising where there is a distinct danger of being caught out
by weather deterioration. Because of their small size such
boats are relatively easily swamped or capsized and, as offered
by the manufacturer, are usually sparsely equipped, with
neither safety gear nor adequate working fittings. Cleats tend
to be too small for the job and are sometimes styled in a way
which reduces their practicality. At first sight some craft of
this type appear to be relatively cheap but this can turn out to
be because the boat is so bare—it may only comprise the GRP
mouldings bonded together, windows, bunks and a cabin
door, with one or two deck fittings added. The inside of such

a boat will look, and feel, cold and clinical especially if the bunks, seats and cabin bulkhead are also made of GRP. It takes a considerable amount of wood trim, linings and other non-GRP fittings to break up the smooth white areas and lose the plastic bath-tub appearance.

Climbing around the cabin to get to the foredeck can be difficult and because of the small size of these boats the angle of heel may be appreciable, especially if someone else happens to move to the same side. It is important to appreciate that the stability of boats of this size is considerably affected by the weight of a number of people on board particularly if they are all standing or some sit on the cabin roof. Capsizes have occurred in situations where the boat was overloaded and two people have gone to the foredeck to lift the anchor, in only moderately rough seas. Being outboard-powered all such cruisers suffer from the inherent vices of these engines, not the least being the fact that the weight of the engine is fairly high up. The above comments highlight the inherent design problems of mini-cruisers but do not relate to a particular craft.

Shetland 536, Birchwood Continental, Marina 16, Micro-Plus 501 and Pacific 550

The Shetland 536 (Plate 1) is one of the best boats of this type. She is the successor to the 535 which is a popular boat. She has sufficient built-in buoyancy to float when swamped and, just as important, is stable when flooded, as the photograph shows. She has a hull form which is a cross between a gull wing and a normal hard-chine hull—the gull wings sit in the water when at rest and greatly enhance stability. With a reasonable proportion of boat in the water compared with the above water profile and a weight of 1290 lb, she steers relatively easily in windy conditions. Inside the cabin there are the normal two berths, sitting headroom and space for a cooker. The helmsman's seat and controls are well positioned but the built-in buoyancy precludes the fitting of cockpit lockers. A 40 h.p. outboard gives 16 knots maximum at a fuel consumption of $3\frac{1}{2}$ gallons an hour. As is normal on this type of boat no provision is made for an anchor, chain and warp, that is, there is neither chain pipe nor chain locker. Apart

1   Shetland 536   Courtesy of Shetland Boats Ltd

from this, to turn a Shetland 536 into a low-priced, safe inshore cruiser one would need to carry a small emergency outboard (for example a Seagull) and the necessary safety gear. Even so the prudent owner will realise the limitations of the boat and use weather forecasts and the boat's high speed to avoid being caught out in rough water. The Shetland has several similar but different sized sisters. Length overall—17 ft 8 in; length waterline— 14 ft; beam—6 ft 10 in; draft—9 in; hull and superstructure—GRP; headroom—4 ft 5 in; builder—Shetland Boats Ltd, Stanton, Bury St Edmunds, Suffolk.

Similar craft include the Birchwood Continental, an 18 ft × 6 ft 10 in cathedral-hulled craft. This hull shape gives more room in the cabin, a larger foredeck and greater stability, but the boat tested was more prone to slam and caused the outboard to cavitate in a tight turn at speed. Birchwood Boat Co, Ltd, Common Road, Huthwaite, Sutton-in-Ashfield, Notts.

The Marina 16 measures 16 ft 3 in × 6 ft 10 in, is a little 'tippy' underfoot and has a rather wide and low inner bulkhead to the outboard well. She gives a relatively good ride and steers well when planing. Marina Boats Ltd., Tything Road, Kinwarton, Alcester.

Like the Shetland, the Micro-Plus 501 has a slightly gull wing hull which increases stability, and a high inner bulkhead to the outboard well. She planes easily. Dimensions— 16 ft 4 in × 6 ft 1 in. Micro-Plus Boats Ltd, Gloucester Trading Estate, Hucclecote, Gloucester.

The Pacific 550 (Plate 2) is a good design with good stability at rest and at speed and particularly wide sidedecks. She measures 18 ft × 6 ft 6 in. Power Marine, Charfleet, Canvey Island, Essex.

2   Pacific 550   Courtesy of Power Marine, T.S.P. (Marine) Ltd

When buying a boat of this type try to have a demonstration trip and take note of the angle of heel when standing on the gunwale, and also go forward and stand on the foredeck. Note the height of the inner bulkhead on the outboard well, the freeboard of the hull and the stiffness of the hull sides by pushing hard in the middle. At planing speed note whether she banks into a turn and whether passengers moving around give any unusual effects.

Misleading 20
This is a fictitious boat, 20 feet in length, with a hard-chine, shallow-vee hull form. It illustrates the basic incompatibility of the design requirements for a boat intended both for canals and the sea. A light keel-less, hard-chine hull with a draft of only a few inches and a canal-restricted beam of 6 ft 10 in is not by any stretch of the imagination the best for sea-work. No argument presented in Chapter 3 points to a hull of this description as being seaworthy or seakindly.

Such a light-displacement, dual-purpose design would lack grip in the water, and when powered for displacement speeds would give the liveliest ride in a seaway of any of the types of hull form. Similarly a hull with shallow vee sections will give the greatest accelerations when planing in a choppy sea. Altogether one can say that a hull form of this type is the last in which one would voluntarily choose to go to sea.

There are several other aspects which degrade the sea-worthiness of such a boat; a high cabin creates windage and top weight; a hogged sheer invites the sea aboard the foredeck; a low bulkhead to the outboard well offers a similar invitation into the cockpit; and the outboard itself has just that small trace of unreliability apart from its relatively high up weight.

Another point to consider is that for sea-work much extra equipment, not required for canal cruising, should be fitted. Where will the anchor and chain go? Will the forward cleat stand up to the tow of a hefty fishing boat? Is there locker space for warps and fenders, and lifejackets, oilskins and spare fuel? Is the transom cut-out wide enough for a small emergency outboard?

On the other hand to cruise the canals demands other qualities and features in a boat. The dual-purpose cruiser may in fact have no design characteristics particularly suited for canal use other than a beam of 6 ft 10 in. Features such as slab sides, little flare, rubbing strakes, a flat bottom and a tapering keel are all desirable for a canal boat but most unsuitable for a fast seaboat.

In other words the design falls between two stools and is neither suitable for the sea *nor* for inland work. If one wants a fast 20 footer for the sea a design like the Draco 2000 is far

more suitable, while for canal work the Dawncraft 21 for
example will give much more satisfaction than a boat intended
for both waters and lacking suitability for either.

Fishing cruisers

Seaworker 22
A 2-berth Fisherman (Plate 3). A true fast-round-bilge hull
form giving a speed of 12 knots with the relatively moderate
power of the $1\frac{3}{4}$ litre Perkins 4108 42 h.p. diesel. With the

3   Seaworker 22   Courtesy of Searider Co Ltd

seakindliness of a round-bilge hull form is combined a speed
double that of displacement craft. The hull itself is shallow
because of the necessarily light displacement, but the inboard
version does have a deep keel (18 in) while the outdrive version
(same engine) has a 9 in deep keel. The high fo'c'sle tends to
catch the wind while the shallow draft forward offers little

sideways resistance. She is fairly well-built but of necessarily light construction. The hull and superstructure are of GRP. The hull is directionally stable and will give a better ride in rough water than any other hull form of this displacement. Accepting the potential danger of the large cockpit, stability is good with the low-down weight of a diesel and lack of top hamper. There is 6 ft 2 in headroom in the wheelhouse with good vision over the bows and single-lever engine controls. The cabin is small—just large enough for two rather small bunks. Wide sidedecks make access to the foredeck easy. No ballast is fitted.

A 65–75 h.p. Ford/Merak 4-cylinder 4 litre diesel is an optional engine and gives 16 knots. It takes up more cockpit space and is a noisier engine than the Perkins 4108 while giving no advantage other than a little extra speed. A larger cabin version is available (the Searider) with two berths, a toilet compartment and a galley. There is also a 32 ft version. Length overall —22 ft; length waterline approx.—19 ft; beam—7 ft 9 in; draft—2 ft 3 in; displacement approx.—$1\frac{1}{4}$ tons; headroom in cabin—4 ft 6 in. Agents—Searider Co. Ltd, 11, Nothe Parade, Weymouth. Builders—W. L. Bussel & Co, Weymouth.

Parker 24, Aquaboat Fisher, Versatility 25, Pearson 26

As one might expect from the board of such an experienced designer as Fred Parker, the Parker 24 (Plate 4) is a well designed, strongly built and nicely finished boat. The GRP hull has a good sheer and a rounded and well flared bow. The flat buttock lines and wide transom allow speeds a little over the hump. With the standard engine—a Perkins 4108 flexibly mounted 42 s.h.p. 4-cylinder diesel—a maximum speed of $8\frac{1}{2}$ knots is achieved with a genuine 7 knots cruising with a low noise level. The engine is effectively noise insulated. Vision forward, steering and handling are first class. With a deep draft along the whole length and a relatively low profile, strong winds have little influence. The cabin has two berths in the bows, port and starboard, a toilet compartment to port and a galley to starboard. Headroom is almost 6 ft. Padded backrests for the bunks are at just the right height for sitting and the cabin is lined with vinyl-covered plywood even on the under-

4   Parker 24

side of the foredeck. Access to the foredeck is made easy by the wide sidedecks (but with a slippery moulded-in tread pattern) and rainwater is piped away from the continuous toe-rail to avoid rain marks down the top sides. Large-angle stability should be good with the wide sidedecks, high coaming and flared sides. 44 gallons of fuel can be carried, enough for half a season of normal usage. The cabin is of GRP and the wheelhouse of timber. No ballast is fitted. Length overall—24 ft; length waterline—21 ft; beam—9 ft 3 in; draft—2 ft 6 in; displacement approx.—$2\frac{1}{4}$ tons. Builders—Parker Boats Ltd, Long Reach, Passage Lane, Warsash, Hants.

Another very similar type of cruiser is the Aquaboat Offshore Fisher. Dimensions are 22 ft × 8 ft 7 in × 2 ft 9 in draft. Again a shapely hull with bold flare, a knuckle and a wide transom. 500 lb of ballast is fitted. The standard engine is a Ford 4·15 litre 72 h.p. diesel giving 11 knots. A Mercedes 42 h.p. 4-cylinder diesel gives about 8 knots. Handling and vision forward are excellent and the side decks are particularly wide. Generous-sized bollards are fitted. The layout is much the same as the Parker but without a toilet compartment. Standard of finish is average. The GRP hull has an 11 oz lay-up on the bottom and 9 oz on sides. Aquaboats Ltd, 261–263, Lymington Road, Highcliffe, Christchurch, Hants.

A slightly larger but still similar cruiser is the Versatility 25. Dimensions are 25 ft × 9 ft 2 in × 2 ft 6 in draft but there is a Mk II version which has an extra foot on the beam and the draft. She is strongly built in GRP (approved by the White Fish Authority) and has 25 cwt of concrete ballast. The bows have a sweeping sheer and good flare and a bar extends from the bottom of the keel to the rudder stock protecting the propeller. The forecabin has full headroom, a toilet compartment and galley space. A wheel shelter is fitted and a $2\frac{1}{2}$ litre Thornycroft 4 cylinder diesel gives about $8\frac{1}{2}$ knots. The GRP mouldings are available or the boat can be partly or fully completed. There is an even nicer looking 30 ft version. Versatility Workboats of Rye, Rye Yacht Centre, Rye, Sussex.

The Pearson 26 (Plate 5) is available with a large forward wheelhouse either open or closed-in at the aft end. The closed-in version effectively makes a large forward cabin with over 6 ft headroom and space for two or even four berths arranged upper and lower. The GRP round-bilge hull is laid-up of 14 oz of CSM. Displacement is about $2\frac{3}{4}$ tons including 1500 lb of ballast. A strong, seaworthy (within the limitations of the

5 *Pearson 26 Courtesy of Pearson Bros Ltd*

large cockpit) and seakindly boat, she is directionably stable and handles easily. Pearson Bros, Ltd, Ford Aerodrome, Arundel, Sussex.

Sea Angler 31 and Aqua-Star 32
The Sea Angler 31 is fitted out very much to a fishing boat standard in that there are only two berths in a spartan cabin, together with a toilet compartment and a galley. All deck fittings are of galvanised steel and are large and robust. No noise insulation is fitted. The hull is round-bilge of quite light displacement with a deep keel, bilge keels and a large rudder. The buttock lines are quite flat and 12–14 knots is achieved with the Perkins 6354 6-cylinder diesel of 115 s.h.p. The freeboard is high and the side decks are wide. Ballast would improve the motion, safety and handling of this boat although at the expense of top speed. The GRP hull is laid-up with 14 oz of CSM with one layer of 24 oz woven roving on the bottom only. The superstructure is 10 oz CSM with a balsa cored

6   Sea Angler 23   Courtesy of R Mitchell & Son

coachroof. Steering, vision and handling are good. The Sea Angler 31 is sold to one specification only and is a handsome, seaworthy (necessarily large cockpit) fishing craft, although with modification it would also make a good family cruiser. Length overall—31 ft; length waterline—28 ft approx.; beam—11 ft; draft—3 ft. Builders—R. Mitchell & Son, Meeching Quarry, Newhaven, Sussex.

Mitchell & Son also make a 23 ft simulated clinker version (Plate 6) with a spartan cabin just sufficient for two vee berths.

A similar cruiser is the Aqua-Star 32 with an 11 ft 6 in beam and 3 ft draft. The cockpit is 17 ft long and the cabin has four berths—two vee berths in the bows and a dinette arrangement —together with a large toilet compartment and galley and stowage space. An aft cabin can be fitted. There is also a 26 ft version. The specifications and even the cabin layout can be tailored to a customer's requirement. Aqua-Glass Reinforced Laminates Ltd, Aqua Works, Stem Lane, New Milton, Hampshire.

Hard-chine fast and slow family cruisers

Maclan 22

The emphasis in this cruiser (Plate 7) is on accommodation. With a length of 22 ft there is comfortable living space for a family of four. There are two vee berths in the bows and a dinette with the galley opposite, and also a fairly large toilet compartment. There is full headroom and a great deal of easily cleaned white melamine-surfaced plywood. The effect is a little clinical. The result of carrying such an amount of accommodation is fairly well disguised in the above-water profile of the boat, but the cockpit is rather small and the tall cabin bulkhead blots out the view forward to passengers. Indeed the vision forward for the helmsman is not very good, especially if the optional wheelhouse top is fitted. The GRP hull is medium to deep vee with the bottom near the chines turned down so that the chines are immersed for half the length of the boat when at rest. Matt and woven rovings are used to give a lay-up of $10\frac{1}{2}$ oz. A 130 h.p. BMW or Volvo petrol out-

7   Maclan 22   Courtesy of Maclan Marine

drive gives about 22 knots maximum with a cruising consumption (still planing) of about 3 gallons an hour. At low speeds
there is the usual outdrive vagueness, but the fairly deeply
immersed keel line does help to reduce sensitivity to wind
compared to a shallow vee hull form. Similarly the ride in
rough water is fairly good and tight turns at high speed are
safe with a pronounced inward bank. For inland waters a
30 h.p. Ford petrol engine can be fitted. Generally the out-
fitting of the boat is to an average standard (I thought there
was room for improvement in the rather small cleats and
navigation lights and indifferent ventilation). The sidedecks
are rather narrow for comfort. There is a 25 ft version. Length
overall—22 ft; length waterline—19 ft 6 in; beam—8 ft 3 in;
draft—1 ft 3 in; displacement—1·6 tons. Builders—Maclan
Marine Ltd, Westwood Industrial Estate, Margate, Kent.

*Dolphin 23, Norman 23, Freeman 23, Seamaster 23, Cleopatra
700, Senior 23 and Eastwood 24*
This type of boat has a shallow vee hard-chine hull, a high
wind-catching profile but spacious, full headroom accommo-

dation for four. A wild ride in rough water is likely because of the light displacement, shallow draft and chine hull. On the other hand a high freeboard and a low-down inboard engine (in most cases) help towards seaworthiness, providing the weight of the top hamper is not too great. Thus cruisers of this type have some limitations for sea work both in terms of safety and comfort. (When powered for planing speeds the shallow vee hull will give a very harsh ride in rough water.) Ballast (about 5 cwt) will help considerably in some cases whether the boat is to be used inshore or inland. (A planing type will not be able to take advantage of ballast.) If the keel is not deep enough at its after end this type of cruiser often exhibits directional instability. Rudders are sometimes too small. Manoeuvring into locks may not be easy especially on a windy day. Some craft have a canal-restricted beam and I stick to my personal reservations about the suitability of this restriction for seawork.

The standard Dolphin 23 has the advantage of planing speeds which will enable the owner to dodge back into shelter quickly if the wind gets up. She has a very shallow vee hull with a draft of only 1 ft 2 in and a small keel. There is full headroom in the cabin (between the head-bashing beams) and living space, berths and stowage for four in a conventional arrangement of dinette and vee-berths in the bows. The whole boat and the cabin interior is nicely made and the cabin is colourful, but the overlarge area of glass may not be to some people's liking. The standard engine is a 90 h.p. OMC petrol outdrive which gives a maximum of 16 knots. Fuel consumption at full throttle would be about $4\frac{1}{2}$ gallons an hour. 16 knots represents a speed: length ratio of 3·6 so the boat is in fact only just planing. From a resistance point of view the hull shape is good for this speed while the ride will be fair. At faster speeds it would give a rough ride. 90 h.p. is excessive for rivers and the smallest 4-cylinder petrol engine would give ample power. Deck fittings and the navigation lights are on the small side. Length overall—22 ft 10 in; length waterline approx.— 19 ft 6 in; beam— 8 ft 10 in; displacement—1·63 tons; hull and superstructure—GRP. Marine and Industrial Engineers (Bursledon) Ltd, Ponsharden, Penryn, Cornwall.

The Norman 23 has a beam of 6 ft 10 in. The draft is 1 ft 5 in and the boat I inspected lacked directional stability. An outboard or an outdrive can be fitted, and the superstructure as well as the hull is of GRP. The cabin layout is similar to that of the Dolphin. Norman Cruisers Ltd, Universal Works, Grains Road, Shaw, Lancashire.

The Freeman 23 (Plate 8) has the advantage of an inboard engine (either diesel or petrol, automotive type) a displacement of 1·5 tons and a keel almost a foot deep at its after end,

8 Freeman 23 Courtesy of Freeman Marine Ltd

and a beam of 7 ft 6 in. All this adds up to a reasonable seaboat. However the rudder is small and the keel does not protect the propeller. The cabin has a conventional layout but with extra large berths and a reasonable window area. The shallow vee hull form gives speeds slightly over the hump, with the standard 30–50 h.p. engine. No noise insulation was fitted to the boat I inspected. John Freeman (Marine) Ltd, Wolvey, Near Hinckley, Leics.

The Seamaster 23 (Plate 9) has a large expanse of cabin window, an outdrive and a wide beam of 9 ft 2 in. Finished to a good standard she can be sensibly powered for speeds up to 20 knots. Other comments as for the Dolphin 23. Seamaster Ltd, 20, Ongar Road, Great Dunmow, Essex.

9   Seamaster 23   Courtesy of Seamaster Ltd

There is also the outdrive-powered 22 ft 9 in × 8 ft 6 in Cleopatra 700 Family Cruiser from the Essex Yacht Builders Ltd, Wallasea Island, Near Rochford, Essex; the Senior 23 with a beam of 8 ft 6 in from the same builders as the Senior 31 and the Eastwood 24 (similar to the Freeman) made by Eastwood Yacht Co, Ltd, Walton Bridge, Walton-on-Thames, Surrey.

Fjordcruiser 27 and Nimbus 26
These two boats come from Norway and Sweden respectively and are hard chine, warped bottom GRP cruisers designed for speed:length ratios of 2½ to 4. Inboard powered they have a fairly deep keel, deep enough in the case of the Nimbus to protect the propeller and rudder. Both cruisers have aft cabins

in which there are two berths. The Fjordcruiser (Plate 10) can be fitted with, for example, a Volvo 6 cylinder 170 h.p. petrol engine which gives a speed of about 22 knots or a 106 h.p. Volvo diesel giving 16 knots and considerably greater economy. She performs with very little fuss or noise, steers well at both low speeds (because of the keel) and high speeds and trims very little considering the semi-planing speeds. The flat after

10   Fjordcruiser 27

sections are responsible for the reasonable trim while they are not liable to come out of the water in heavy weather and slam back because of the moderate speed length ratio. The bows are deeply veed—hence the warped bottom. The main cabin has two vee berths in the bows, a settee berth and a toilet compartment, all fitted out in a rich and colourful style. The galley is situated in the cockpit which is flush-decked over the engine. Length overall—27 ft; length waterline—25 ft; beam—9 ft 10 in; draft—2 ft 6 in; displacement—2·3 tons: Builders—A/S Fjord Plast Postbox 133, 4801, Arendal, Norway. UK Agents—Eastwood Yacht Company Ltd, Walton Bridge, Walton-on-Thames, Surrey.

The Nimbus 26 is similar except that the forecabin is smaller with just two berths and a toilet compartment while the cockpit (partially covered by a wheelshelter) has the galley and a dinette. A fitted canopy covers the rest of the cockpit at night. A 75 h.p. Volvo diesel gives about 14 knots. The remarks on ride and handling of the Fjordcruiser also apply to the Nimbus.

The hull is GRP and the deck and cabin GRP foam sandwich construction. Internal finish is average and the engine noise level rather high. Length overall—26 ft; length waterline —24 ft 6 in approx.; beam—9 ft 6 in; draft—2 ft 8 in. UK Agents—Bristol Channel Yachts, May's Marina, Harbour Road, Lydney, Glos. and Starlight Marine, Welsh Bridge, Shrewsbury, Shropshire.

Waterland 75
This Dutch cruiser has a shallow vee hard-chine hull, but the inherent vices of such a hull are partially overcome by a long, reasonably deep keel—deep enough at its after end to protect the propeller and rudder of a conventional inboard installation. Even though primarily designed and offered for cruising in sheltered waters, the Waterland 75 is more seaworthy than many shallow vee hard-chine boats claimed to be suitable for inland and offshore use. The fact that only inboard engines are supplied contributes to this. A gentle sheer, flared and raked bows and a wide beam add their quota of seaworthiness. Ford petrol engines or diesels up to 70 h.p. can be fitted which, while not giving planing speeds, give speeds in excess of the hump. The engine is installed under the cockpit sole and the compartment is ventilated by an electric fan. The aft cabin has two quarter berths and makes an excellent children's cabin. The main cabin has a dinette to starboard, a toilet compartment and galley opposite, and two vee berths in the bows. Headroom is 6 ft 2 in and the standard of finish is good and the furniture reasonably solid. Stowage space is plentiful. Most of the equipment fitted is reasonably sized and substantial, for instance the gunwale fender and the 22 gallon fuel tank, but the pulpit and the cleats are on the small side. No ballast is fitted and the light displacement of 1·7 tons means that she will be quite lively in rough water. The GRP hull and super-

structure appear to be moulded to a good standard. The helmsman has good vision forward and the boat is directionally stable. The Waterland 75 has two similar sisters—the 70 (23 ft 6 in) and 85 (27 ft 4 in). Length overall—24 ft; length waterline—20 ft 3 in; beam—8 ft 10 in; draft—2 ft 4 in. Builder—Afd, Watersport, Joan Muyskenweg 14, Amsterdam. Agents in UK include Toughs Shipyards Ltd, Teddington.

Fairline Fury and Cleopatra 850
The unusual feature of the Fairline Fury (Plate 11) is the flying bridge. By troughing the cabin top, a walkway is formed to reach the low-seated steering position where there is room for two. The view is excellent and also one is away from the noise

11   Fairline Fury

of the engine. Access is by a sloping ladder on the aft bulkhead and in calm water there is no difficulty or insecurity when climbing up to the wheel. The GRP hull is laid-up with $9\frac{1}{2}$ oz of glass including a layer of woven roving. The space under the plywood cabin floor is filled with polyurethane foam. The hull form has bottom sections aft comprising three Us, and the ride is quite good. With toughened glass windows and a small cockpit the Fury is a seaworthy boat.

The accommodation comprises a small two-berth cabin up forward and a large full-headroom saloon with a dinette, a toilet compartment and a long galley section with plenty of stowage and working space. The whole interior is tastefully fitted out with a pleasing mixture of plastic surfaces and wood grain. The Fury steers well at high speed and banks into turns. At low speeds the familiar outdrive vagueness is apparent. A single 130 h.p. (SAE) Volvo outdrive gives 17–18 knots, while twins give 26–29 knots together with twin engine safety at sea (she steers satisfactorily on one engine). Length overall—24 ft 9 in; length waterline—21 ft 6 in; beam—8 ft 9 in; draft—1 ft 2 in; displacement—2·0–2·3 tons. Builders—Fairline Boats Ltd, Oundle, Near Peterborough.

A similar boat by the same designer is the Cleopatra 850 International which measures 27 ft 10 in × 9 ft 4 in. On the same hull the builders also produce a version called the 850 Family Cruiser (Plate 12) which has an interesting wheelhouse-cum-cabin arrangement. The enclosed wheelhouse has full

*2 *850 Family Cruiser* *Courtesy of Essex Yacht Builders Ltd*

headroom and measures approximately 7 ft square. Inside, apart from the steering position, is a dinette and a single upper berth. Large doors in the after bulkhead can open the wheelhouse to the cockpit when the weather is good. The cockpit floor is flush with the wheelhouse floor and the arrangement gives the best of both worlds. The forward cabin has two vee berths, a galley and a toilet compartment. All the fitting-out is to a good and colourful standard. Hull lay-up is 18 oz on the bottom and 12 oz on the topsides. The hull shape is shallow to medium vee and the ride is reasonably good in choppy water by virtue of her size and 3·2 tons displacement, but in larger seas the pounding would force one to slow down. Volvo petrol or diesel outdrives can be fitted. Builders—Essex Yacht Builders Ltd, Wallasea Island, Near Rochford, Essex.

Kingswift 26 and Orrskar 26
A British cruiser from the Littlehampton yard famous for its lifeboats is the Kingswift 26 (Plate 13). Originally this cruiser was built in wood but she now has a GRP hull. However,

13   Kingswift 26   Courtesy of William Osborne Ltd

extensive use of varnished timber together with a traditionally-shaped superstructure, still give the traditional flavour (the decks are teak-faced plywood). She measures 26 ft × 9 ft 10 in, has a shallow to medium vee hull and is powered normally by twin 130 h.p. BMW petrol outdrives, which should give about 25 knots. The cabin has four berths, 6 ft headroom, a galley and a toilet compartment (access gained from the cockpit). The standard of workmanship is high, but vision forward from the wheel is not very good. The boat trims bows-up too much, especially at 10–15 knots—probably just a matter of tuning. William Osborne Ltd, Arun Shipyard, Littlehampton, Sussex.

The Swedish Orrskar has a medium vee hull strongly made in GRP, berths for six in a full headroom cabin, and a spacious toilet compartment. The galley is in the cockpit, Scandinavian style, inside a large wheel shelter. Powered by a Volvo out-drive, the remarkable thing about this cruiser is the noise insulation; she is probably the quietest production cruiser of all. The engine (a 130 or 170 h.p. petrol or 106 h.p. diesel) is flexibly mounted inside a heavily insulated box which is in turn flexibly mounted to the hull; there is also an acoustic hood on the transom over the outdrive leg. She measures 26 ft 7 in × 9 ft 2 in × 1 ft 2 in draft, with a displacement of 2·4 tons. UK Agents—Molde Batservice AS, Low Risby, Roxby, Scunthorpe, Lincs.

Senior 31

The Senior 31 (Plate 14) is an example of a shallow-to-medium vee hard-chine hull form. At amidships the deadrise is about 15° reducing to about 9° at the transom. But though the hull itself is shallow there is a timber keel which tapers deeper at the aft end. Nevertheless the draft is only 2 ft 3 in. She is directionally stable. This is a large boat so 20 knots represents a speed: length ratio of only 3·8, in other words she is only just planing properly at this speed. She is best powered for speeds of less than 25 knots when the shallow vee hull gives an advantage over a deeper vee in terms of power required. On the other hand the windage is large and the draft shallow; the motion will be relatively wild in rough water when forced to slow down.

Engines may be outdrive or inboard, single or twin, diesel or petrol, 100 h.p. giving about 13 knots and 200 h.p. about 23 knots. The GRP hull has a 10 oz bottom and 8 oz topsides, but there are longitudinal stiffeners at quite close spacing.

14   Senior 31

In the cabin there is a dinette and large toilet compartment to port, and a single berth, galley and wardrobe to starboard; the forecabin has two vee berths. There is full headroom, and space for such items as a refrigerator and a water heater. Vision forward from the large wheel shelter is not very good when the bows lift at 10–15 knots. The hull and superstructure mouldings are fitted out by several other firms. Smaller versions with similar lines are also produced by Senior Marine—26, 23 and 20 ft long. Length overall—31 ft; length waterline—27 ft 6 in; beam—9 ft 8 in; displacement— 3·6 tons. Builders—Senior Marine Ltd, Kemps Shipyard, Quayside Road, Bitterne Manor, Southampton.

Round-bilge displacement family cruisers

Nelson 18, Sturgeon and Aqua-Star 19
If one is looking for a 16–18 ft 2-berth cruiser and is not
interested in tearing around at high speed, common sense
suggests that there must be more suitable designs of boat
than those mentioned earlier simply turned into low speed
boats by adding a small outboard. Desirable features such as
an inboard engine and a much heavier, deeper-draft round-
bilge hull can be realised. Such a cruiser can be made much
more seaworthy especially if ballast is added and while the
boat will not skitter around in strong winds on inland waters
the draft will not be too great. The boat will be directionally
stable and handle well. Such boats are relatively rare nowadays, but the GRP Nelson 18 and Halmatic 18 are good
examples. The hulls are strongly built by Tyler Boat Co, Ltd,
and Halmatic Ltd, respectively (Figure 72), and completed by
several boat yards. They measure 18 ft × 6 ft 10 in and have a

72   Halmatic 18

deep keel protecting the propeller and rudder giving a draft of
just under 2 ft; displacement is about 1 ton. Power can be anything from a small single-cylinder petrol or diesel engine (5 h.p.
Petter diesel or Stuart-Turner petrol engine, for example) to a 4-
cylinder 30 h.p. automotive petrol engine giving about 8 knots.
The cabin has two berths, and a toilet compartment is possible.
With ballast fitted the Nelson 18 can be made into a most
seaworthy cruiser for her length. The graceful sheer is in direct
contrast to the modern trend of flat or hogged sheer. Tyler
Boat Co, Ltd, 1–10, Sovereign Way, Tonbridge, Kent, and
Halmatic Ltd, Havant, Hants.

Plate 15 shows the Halmatic hull completed by Mariner's Boatyard, Bosham, Sussex. The construction is to a good standard with plywood being used for the cabin. About 25 have been built and many are to be seen afloat in the area, and very handsome little cruisers they look.

15   Ocean 18   Courtesy of Mariners Boatyard

There is also the GRP Sturgeon cruiser, 16 ft long by 6 ft 6 in beam with a draft of 1 ft 3 in. 210 lb of ballast is incorporated and a large rope gunwale fender is supplied. Timber trim is evident and there is a traditional mahogany wheel. A 6·6 h.p. Petter diesel in a sound-proofed box will give 6 knots and a laughably small fuel consumption. Latham & Son, Weston Point Boatyard, Sandbanks Road, Poole, Dorset.

Another example is the GRP Aqua-Star 19. She measures 19 ft × 7 ft with a draft of 1 ft 10 in and is robustly built with a properly sound-proofed Yanmar diesel, a small wheelhouse and a 2-berth cabin. A good sized rudder is fitted and in fact all the equipment is of generous proportions, including the bollards. Available with many fittings such as a cockpit canopy and a sea-toilet, or just hull and superstructure. Aqua-Star Reinforced Laminates Ltd, Aqua Works, Stem Lane, New Milton, Hants.

Atlanta Sea Rider and Parkstone Bay 21
The hull of the Sea Rider (Plate 16) is the 19 ft 6 in Colvic moulded in GRP by Ardleigh Laminated Plastics Co Ltd, Weston Road, Industrial Estate East, Witham, Essex. It is a

6   Atlanta Sea Rider   Courtesy of Atlanta Marine

popular hull and is fitted out by many builders. It is an example of the mock displacement or light displacement form mentioned in Chapter 2 i.e. it has a light displacement ($1-1\frac{1}{2}$ tons) yet the slope of the buttock lines and waterlines aft preclude speeds over the hump. The hull shape can be considered as an alternative to the shallow vee hard-chine form, and as such is a far preferable proposition where only displacement speeds are being considered. The hull has good freeboard and beam and generally a seakindly shape (within the limitations of the light displacement). Atlanta Marine sensibly deepen the keel (the standard hull has a draft of 1 ft 6 in) and add bilge keels, a large transom-hung rudder and 3 cwt of ballast. A 10 h.p. Bukh diesel gives about 6 knots. It is a single-cylinder flexibly mounted electric start engine, and consumes about 3 pints an hour cruising at about 5 knots which represents about 13 m.p.g. The maximum sensible engine power is about 25 h.p. The wheel shelter is roomy with full headroom and the cabin has two vee berths and a galley area. A toilet can be fitted underneath a berth. Headroom is about 4 ft 3 in and joinery work is to a good standard, but the cabin is unlined and rather bare. She is directionally stable and handles well. Length overall—21 ft 1 in; length waterline—18 ft 4 in; beam—7 ft 4 in; draft—2 ft 3 in. Builders—Atlanta Marine, Arnside Road, Hambledon Road Industrial Estate, Waterlooville, Portsmouth.

Also available from Ardleigh Laminated Plastics is a 26 ft 6 in hull of similar shape. The beam is 8 ft 8 in and draft 2 ft 6 in with a design displacement of 3·8 tons. Again this hull is completed by many builders as a fishing launch or a motor cruiser. With a waterline length of 24 ft 8 in, speeds up to 9 knots are possible. A long raised GRP fo'c'sle deck is also available giving 6 ft headroom in the cabin and space for a main cabin area and a small forecabin.

A similar traditionally styled craft is the 21 ft Parkstone Bay. Three versions are available with different cabin lengths. The beam is 7 ft 3 in and draft 1 ft 10 in. The hull is GRP and similar in shape to the Colvic, but the decks and superstructures are made in timber. A Mercedes 40 h.p. diesel gives 9 knots. Mitchell and Sons Ltd, Turks Lane, Sandbanks Road, Parkstone, Poole, Dorset.

Dauntless and Chesford

These cruisers are examples of traditional clinker construction coupled with traditional lines and engines. Dauntless make versions from 20 ft to 24 ft. The smallest has dimensions 20 ft × 7 ft 6 in × 1 ft 7 in draft and a two-berth cabin with sitting headroom, the berths being on each side with a folding table on the centreline. There is space for a toilet in the fore-peak. A Stuart-Turner 2-cylinder 2-stroke petrol engine is installed in the cockpit and one steers by a tiller. Speed is about $6\frac{1}{2}$ knots. The 24 ft cruiser version (Plate 17) has two cabins with two berths in each, a toilet compartment

17 Dauntless 24   Courtesy of Dauntless Company

and galley, a wheel shelter and a flexibly mounted BLMC 1·5 litre 4-cylinder 30 h.p. inboard diesel giving about $7\frac{1}{2}$ knots. The engine drives through a vee drive thus obviating an engine box obstructing the entrance to the cabin. Construction is with an oak keel and deadwood $3\frac{1}{2}$ in thick, an oak stem 3 in thick, steamed ash timbers $1\frac{1}{4}$ in $\times \frac{7}{8}$ in and $\frac{1}{2}$ in thick mahogany clinker planks in one length. Engine bearers are 2 in thick and the cabin sides $\frac{3}{4}$ in solid mahogany. The decks are either 5 in $\times$ $\frac{5}{8}$ in fir planking or plywood, both covered with Trackmark. All fastenings are of copper or brass and four coats of paint or varnish are applied. All planking and timbers of all the

Dauntless craft are treated with Cuprinol wood preserver. Length overall—24 ft; length waterline—22 ft approx.; beam— 8 ft 6 in; draft—2 ft. Builders—The Dauntless Co, Canvey Island, Essex.

Timber construction has many advantages, but considerably more maintenance is required. On the other hand buying a new boat is a different proposition in this respect from buying an older wooden cruiser. Providing she is covered up in the winter and always has the cockpit cover up during the summer when not in use, a modicum of care and maintenance will keep her looking new for many years. If the owner is fairly handy he can gradually improve the finish of the boat, especially internally, and can alter and make improvements which he may hesitate to do on a GRP cruiser. It is also often true that a wooden boat is cheaper initially.

Chesford Marine build 18 ft and 23 ft cruisers. The 18 footer has two berths and a low-height doghouse. Steering is by tiller. A Stuart Turner inboard is fitted. She measures 18 ft × 6 ft 3 in × 1 ft 8 in. The 23 footer has a good beam of 9 ft and a draft of 2 ft 3 in. Again the cabin has two berths. Mahogany is used for the clinker construction with oak for the keel. Galvanised bilge keels are fitted. Finish is a little austere but this is reflected in the price and can be improved in due course by attention from the owner.

Myra 21 and Saga 20
These two boats are unusual in having pointed sterns. The Norwegian Myra 21 has a delightful sheer and raked, well flared bows giving a broad foredeck. Constructed in GRP she has some concrete ballast and an inboard engine. The sides forward are clinker-style and the underside of the hull aft is flat, giving a chine just under the waterline. The propeller and rudder are protected by a keel and keel bar. Altogether a seaworthy boat, the only limitation being imposed by the open cockpit. The forecabin has two vee berths, sitting headroom and a wardrobe. A toilet can be fitted under one berth. The galley is under the wheelshelter and with the fitted canopy up, two more berths are available in the cockpit. The engine box unfortunately obstructs the cockpit. Steering and handling,

and vision from the wheel, are good. There is a nylon covered hatch in the wheelhouse roof. Engines of 15 to 25 h.p. give 7 to 8 knots and a probable cruising fuel consumption of around ½ gallon an hour. The Myra has a sister, the 23, which has an aft cabin and a transom stern. Length overall— 20 ft 8 in; length waterline—18 ft approx.; beam—7 ft 3 in; draft—2 ft 6 in; displacement—1·2 tons. Builders—Myra Plast, Kristiansund, Norway. UK Agents—Starlight Marine, Welsh Bridge, Shrewsbury, Shropshire.

A boat of similar sensible proportions but having different features is the Saga 20 (Plate 18). She is traditionally styled with a simulated clinker GRP hull and an open-ended cabin— there is no bulkhead. This gives more space for day use while a hooped canopy gives protection if it rains and turns the boat into a camping craft at night. The pretty hull has a seakindly shape with a deep draft, flare and sheer. There is little top hamper and she handles in the normal viceless manner of a displacement boat. A small Volvo diesel or petrol engine gives 6¼ knots. A petrol engine is a more logical choice with its lesser noise and vibration while still giving low running costs at less than ½ gallon an hour at a quiet speed:length ratio of 1·0 for which the pointed stern is ideal. A far more economical and seaworthy craft than a similar sized hard chine outboard powered cruiser. Length—20 ft; beam—7 ft 3 in; draft— 2 ft 4 in; displacement—0·9 tons. Builders—Selje Bruk A/S Norway. UK Agents—Starlight Marine, Welsh Bridge, Shrewsbury, Shropshire.

The Saga 27 (Plate 19) is similar in style to the Myra 21.

Island Plastics 23 foot

Island Plastics Ltd only build the GRP hull which is then fitted out by numerous boat builders. It can be fitted out as a 4-berth motor cruiser with separate toilet compartment and a galley (as in Plate 20) or a 2-berth fisherman, or, of course, as a one-off design. The hull form is rather like a Scottish fishing boat but shallower with flatter buttocks. The displacement is therefore less but another knot can be achieved. Thus with a 40 h.p. diesel 7½/8 knots is possible. It is a beamy and spacious hull despite the canoe stern, and makes a large boat for its

18   Saga 20   Courtesy of Starlight Marine Ltd (Agents of Saga)

19   Saga 27   Courtesy of Starlight Marine Ltd (Agents of Saga)

20   IP23   Courtesy of Island Plastics Ltd

length. It is directionally stable and, with such high bows, very dry. Basically a seaworthy and seakindly hull, but the free-board is rather low just aft of amidships, which together with the wide beam means that the angle of flooding-in is small. Wide side decks and high coamings to the cockpit are there-fore desirable. The tumblehome at the after end means that quarter rubbing strakes need to be fitted. The deep keel aft and canoe stern should reduce the chance of broaching. Obviously only an inboard engine installation can be fitted, the sensible maximum being about 40 h.p. GRP superstructure mouldings for the motor cruiser and fisherman are available from Island Plastics. It is possible to add an external iron keel and steadying sails—in fact the hull can be completed as a motor sailer. The lines of the IP 23 hull are shown at the end of Chapter 2. Length overall—23 ft; length waterline—20 ft 3 in; beam—9 ft; draft—2 ft 7 in; displacement— approx. 2 tons. Builders—Island Plastics Ltd, Edward Street, Ryde, Isle of Wight.

Albin 25
This Swedish cruiser (Plate 21) is well designed and well built. The GRP hull is round-bilge and of light displacement, cor-responding to the mock displacement hull shape mentioned in Chapter 2 although it could almost be called a fast round-bilge shape. It was tank tested and ran very cleanly up to a speed: length ratio of 2·3 (11 knots with the 36 h.p. Volvo 3-cylinder diesel). The bilge keels and keel endings and the rudder are carefully faired-in to reduce drag and there is an effective knuckle just above the waterline forward. This attention to the hull shape and fairing also gives a high m.p.g. of 16·5 when cruising. At the economical speed of $5\frac{1}{2}$ knots the consumption is $\frac{1}{3}$ gallon an hour with the engine revolving at 1200 r.p.m. and the propeller at 650 r.p.m. The Albin is one of the few motor cruisers which have proper noise insulation features such as an encapsulated engine with two air ducts leading to ventilators on the aft deck. It is also notable that a most informative handbook is supplied giving details of construc-tion, performance and maintenance. The forecabin has two vee berths, a galley and a toilet compartment and is fitted out

21   Albin 25   Courtesy of Albin Marine Ltd

with teak-faced plywood with good stowage spaces, back-rests and attractive linings. The aft cabin is ideal for two children. Access forward is easy and the boat steers and handles very well. Vision, whether seated on the bench seat or standing up through the sun roof, is good. Everything about the Albin 25 points to a seaworthy and seakindly craft—notwithstanding the light displacement and lack of ballast. A mast and sails (90 sq ft) can be fitted for steadying purposes. There is also a fishing version which does not have the aft cabin, and a 21 ft version which is similar but has no aft cabin and a 2-cylinder

slow running Albin petrol engine. Length overall—25 ft;
length waterline—22 ft 2 in; beam— 8 ft 6 in; draft— 2 ft 4 in;
displacement—1·6 tons. Builders—Albin Marine A B, Kristine-
hamn, Sweden. UK Agents—Albin Marine Ltd, 180E, Bridge
Road, Sarisbury Green, Southampton, Hants.

Viksund 27
Here is an example of a true displacement hull form. The hull
lies deep in the water and carries 0·4 tons of ballast—about
11 per cent of the weight of the boat—sufficient for steadying
sails (sloop rig) which will give some propulsion if the engine
fails. The floodable volume represented by the self-draining
cockpit is small and the cockpit coamings are high. The hull
has a shapely sheer, good freeboard in relation to the beam, a
deeply immersed propeller and a large rudder. All these
features together with toughened glass windows and ballast and
the heavy GRP construction add up to a very seaworthy boat
(Figure 73). The Volvo 25 h.p. 2-cylinder diesel is installed
underneath the cockpit sole and there is a steering position inside
the cabin as well as in the cockpit. Thus the helmsman has the
best of both worlds whatever the weather. The cabin has full

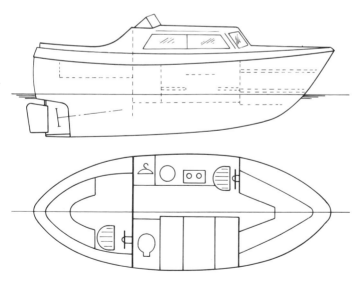

73   Viksund 27

headroom and is fitted out and lined to the usual high Scandinavian standard producing homely and colourful accommodation. The forecabin has the usual vee berths but above these a wide shelf acts as a further two berths suitable for children and as a backrest when sitting on the lower berths. Maximum speed is definitely limited by the pointed stern to about $7\frac{1}{2}$ knots with a quiet cruise of 5 knots. Handling is slow but sure and because of the low profile and deep draft she is unaffected by a strong beam wind. Viksund is supplied comprehensively equipped. Notable are the large, correctly sited navigation lights and the hefty all-round gunwale fender. Like many Scandinavian boats there is no provision for an anchor and chain. There is also a 31 ft version. Length overall—26 ft 6 in; length waterline—23 ft 6 in; beam—9 ft 4 in; draft—3 ft 7 in; displacement $3\frac{1}{2}$ tons. Builders—Viksund Bat A/S 5302, Strusshamn, Norway. Agents in UK—Viksund Boats, Low Risby, Roxby, Near Scunthorpe, Lincs.

Hardy 8·25
A true heavy displacement hull with a transom stern, deep draft, curvacious sheer and good flare (Figure 74). As the weight of the complete boat does not by any means equal the displacement of the hull, 1·2 tons of ballast has to be fitted to bring her down to her marks. The displacement is 4·7 tons. A fair spread of auxiliary sail is thus possible. Together with toughened glass

74   Hardy 8·25

windows, wide sidedecks and high coamings, this boat constitutes the ultimate in pleasure-boat seaworthiness and seakindliness. Naturally the top speed is limited to about $7\frac{1}{2}$ knots however powerful the engine. Twin or single inboards can be fitted underneath the cockpit sole and a power of 40–80 h.p. is suitable. For a 27 footer the cabin is small: one arrangement is to have four berths, one up, one down, port and starboard, the upper folding down to form the back-rests to the lower during the day. Then there is space for a large forward toilet compartment and a galley and wardrobe just inside the main cabin door. There is full headroom. Tylers, who mould the hull, are one of the leading GRP boat hull moulders in the UK. The Hardy 8·25 can be supplied as a bare hull (which weighs 0·8 tons) or with ballast incorporated, bulkheads fitted, two GRP tanks, all stringers, girders and bunk bases, cabin wheelhouse and cockpit mouldings fitted. The lines plan is shown at the end of Chapter 2. Length overall—27 ft; length waterline—24 ft 6 in; beam—9 ft; draft— 3 ft 1 in. Moulders—Tyler Boat Co, Ltd, Tonbridge, Kent.

Deep vee sports cruisers

Draco 2000, Skagerak and Fjord 21

The Draco 2000 (Plate 22) is a Norwegian boat having a genuine deep vee hull (23° deadrise) featuring turned-down chines to give better stability at rest. Outdrive powered, she exhibits the usual vagueness in steering at very slow speeds. The hump is pronounced after which the take-off is spectacular and the boat levels off and accelerates up to top speed. The Volvo 130 h.p. 4-cylinder petrol outdrive gives about 30 knots, and the Volvo 75 h.p. 4-cylinder diesel about 20 knots. The performance of the diesel is markedly sluggish compared to that of the petrol engine and the noise level high. Simulated clinker topsides and moulded-in spray rails on the bottom stiffen the already rigid GRP hull (the bottom is $\frac{3}{8}$ in thick). The ride of any small boat at high speeds in rough water is harsh but the Draco's ride is as good as any and naturally far better than shallow vee varieties. The boat banks into tight turns steeply

22   Draco 2000   Courtesy of Dell Quay Sales Ltd

and safely with no cavitation. Powered with the 130 h.p. (SAE) Volvo, fuel consumption is about $6\frac{1}{2}$ gallons an hour at full throttle, but throttled back to 3800 r.p.m. (still planing) the consumption drops to 3 gallons an hour. Fuel capacity is 33 gallons. The engine is tucked away under a seat across the transom and the engine compartment has an extraction fan which you switch on for a minute before starting the engine. There are two berths in the small cabin which is fully lined and nicely fitted out with teak trim. A toilet can be fitted under one bunk. Details on the boat are carefully thought out and shelves and stowage spaces are plentifully arranged. Going forward and working on the foredeck is not very easy. There is also a 30 ft Draco. Length overall—20 ft; beam—7 ft 7 in; draft—13 in; displacement—0·9 tons. Builders—Draco AS, Kare, Drangsholt, Flekkefjord, Norway. UK Agents—Northshore Yacht Agencies, Itchenor Shipyard, Chichester, Sussex.

A similar boat—also Norwegian—is the 21 ft Skagerak. A Volvo 130 h.p. (SAE) petrol outdrive gives about 28 knots. The beam is 8 ft and the displacement about 1·0 ton. Again the deep vee hull gives more grip in the water at low speeds, a better ride at high speeds and less tendency to broach than comparable shallow vee boats. Three versions are available, one which is open, one with a good wheel shelter added and, lastly, one with a proper cabin (which spoils the appearance). Builders—Skagerak A/S Nedre Slottsgt, 15, Oslo 1 Norway. UK Agents—Boat Showrooms of London Ltd, 286–290, Kensington High Street, London, W.14.

Yet another similar and streamlined-looking Norwegian cruiser is the Fjord 21 weekender. A 170 h.p. (SAE) Volvo petrol outdrive gives 30 knots. The cockpit sole is raised to allow a small two-berth cabin (really more of a cubby hole) underneath; this is entered through a hole in the bulkhead. Rather cramped for adults but spacious enough for children. The main cabin is particularly attractive in appearance and plushly fitted out. There is a separate small toilet compartment and a galley and plenty of stowage space. An ingenious modern design, superior in handling, ride and safety to comparable shallow vee designs. A/S Fjord Plast, Postbox 133, 4801, Arendel, Norway. UK Agents—Eastwood Yacht Co, Ltd, Walton Bridge, Walton-on-Thames, Surrey.

Triana 25

The Triana (Plate 23) is an example of a true race boat deep vee hull turned into a cruiser. The hull has a heavily hogged sheer with a long bow overhang and of course a deadrise of around 25° right back to the transom. In fact the hull form for the Triana was drawn by Renato Levi who, more than anyone else, was the pioneer of the 'deep vee'. Twin petrol outdrives (usually Volvo) will propel this craft at up to 40 knots (a speed:length ratio of $8\frac{1}{2}$). The sides even amidships are appreciably flared and by the time the hull meets the water the actual waterline breadth is low. The inherent vices of the extreme deep vee, tippiness at rest and a tendency to loll over at high speed, especially in strong beam winds, are possibly present in this craft. There are two vee berths in the bows, a dinette, a toilet compartment and a galley, all well finished, as indeed is the whole boat. The GRP hull moulding is by Tylers. Length overall—25 ft; length waterline—21 ft 6 in; beam—9 ft; draft—1 ft 7 in. Builders—Triana Yachts, Cogdean Elm, Wimborne, Dorset.

23   *Triana Tropica   Courtesy of Triana Boats Ltd*

Fjord 30 Weekender

The Fjord 30 (Figure 75) is an example of a safe but high powered deep vee sports cruiser. Built in Norway she is sleek in appearance with a low profiled cabin which yet gives 6 ft headroom. Twin 170 h.p. (SAE) Volvo petrol outdrives give a maximum of 26–29 knots at a consumption of 20 gallons an hour. The best cruising speed occurs at 4000 r.p.m. giving 19 knots, at a consumption of 10 gallons an hour and an m.p.g. of 1·9. She trims to about 6° at this speed but flattens out to 3° at full speed. The ride, steering and vision at high speed are good and, on such a large boat, the deep vee's inherent tippiness is not noticeable. There is a raised bridge deck under which there is a small two-berth cabin; this is reasonably spacious. Forward of this is a large area with a fully fitted toilet compartment and galley and then in the bows there is a dinette arrangement. Thus four people can live aboard in comfort and possibly an extra one or two children. The standard and thoughtfulness of the fitting-out is typically Scandinavian with colour, plenty of stowage and complete linings. Navigation lights which meet International Regulations are fitted, and an electric blower for the engine compartment. The GRP mouldings are strong and well finished. A framed fitted canopy folds neatly in front of the windscreen. All windows are of toughened glass. Two

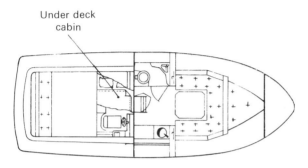

Under deck cabin

75   Fjord 30 Weekender

reasonably sized cleats are fitted to the foredeck together with a self-draining chain locker. Length overall—29 ft 3 in; length waterline—25 ft approx.; beam—10 ft 8 in; draft—2 ft approx.; displacement—4·2 tons. Builders—A/S Fjord Plast Postbox 133, 4801, Arendal, Norway. UK Agents—Eastwood Yacht Co, Ltd, Walton Bridge, Walton-on-Thames, Surrey.

Fairey Fantome
A superbly designed and built craft—fast, seaworthy and lavishly furnished and equipped, impressive in looks and performance (Plate 24). Of course one pays dearly for this sort of quality. The hull is truly deep vee with a displacement of about 5·1 tons. Twin 180 h.p. 6-cylinder Ford diesels give 28 knots maximum with a genuine cruising speed of 24 knots which can be maintained well offshore in conditions where 20 to 25 ft cruisers would be crawling home. Steering at speed in rough water is very good while at slow speeds the low profile and deep vee hull give rise to no difficulties in strong winds. Manoeuvrability in harbour with twin screws and rumbling diesels is impressive. The forward cabin has two berths, a

large galley space and a toilet compartment, while the aft cabin has two berths. Four people can live on board comfortably.

The propellers and rudders project below the bottom of the boat so one has to be careful not to run aground. Fuel consumption at 25 knots is about 14 gallons an hour (2 m.p.g.).

24   Fairey Fantome   Courtesy of Fairey Marine Ltd

Tanks containing 100 gallons are fitted. There are several other similar Fairey cruisers, some of them with hot-moulded timber hull construction, the GRP Fantome being a fairly recent design. Length overall—32 ft 2½ in; length waterline—28 ft approx.; beam—9 ft 9 in; draft—2 ft 10 in. Builders—Fairey Marine Ltd, Hamble, Southampton.

Large fast round-bilge cruisers

Apollo, Weymouth 32 and Keith Nelson 34
These boats have fast round-bilge hulls (Figure 16). The

sections forward are deeply veed blending into straight flat buttock lines aft. A spray chine is incorporated. A deep keel gives directional stability, counteracts leeway and to some extent protects the propellers and rudders. Powered for speed: length ratios of 2 to 4 these boats do not properly plane but give a comfortable ride with little tendency to slam; overpowered, they squat by the stern and become wet. Large twin inboard diesels are the normal form of propulsion and, with such a large hull, the accommodation is luxurious and can cater for the living requirements of at least four people. Cruisers like these can make fast offshore passages at average speeds of 10–15 knots in comfort knowing that conditions will have to become very severe before speed has to be slackened for comfort or safety. In really rough water this hull form will be able to carry on at a fair speed when a planing boat of comparable size, even one of the deep vee variety, will be slamming and wallowing dangerously at low speeds. Naturally the other aspects of seaworthiness such as strong windows and a small protected cockpit must be incorporated to take advantage of the seaworthiness of the hull. Keith Nelson are well known for their pilot boats and service launches.

The Danish-built Apollo has an aft cabin and twin 85 h.p. Perkins diesels under the centre cockpit floor. She measures 32 ft overall (28 ft 7 in at the water line), 10 ft 6 in beam and 2 ft 5 in draft, with a displacement of $4\frac{1}{2}$ tons. Maximum speed is about 14 knots. Carl Zeigler Yacht Agency, 22, New Quebec St, London, W.1. Builders are Klaus Baess, 21 Livjaegergade DK 2100, Copenhagen, Denmark.

Weymouth measures 32 ft overall (30 ft at the waterline), 10 ft 10 in beam and 2 ft 9 in draft with a displacement of $8\frac{1}{2}$ tons. The hull is moulded by Halmatic Ltd. With two 152 h.p. Perkins diesels she does about 20 knots. James and Caddy Ltd, Granby Industrial Estate, Weymouth, Dorset.

Perhaps the best known boats of this type are the Keith Nelson launches. The 34 ft version (the smallest) (Plate 25) is moulded by the Tyler Boat Co, Ltd, Tonbridge, Kent, including a deck/superstructure moulding which gives a cabin with living space for four and a large wheel shelter and cockpit.

Canal cruisers

Dawncraft 22, Burland 26, Dobson 24, Nauticus, Buckingham and Charnwood

The Dawncraft 22 is an out-and-out canal cruiser. The hull shape is box-like with four rubbing strakes protecting the GRP hull. There are two long bilge keels which probably help to give the craft a grip on the water, as otherwise the draft is 14 in. In order to keep the propeller of the outboard as high as possible a tunnel stern is incorporated, together with an internal outboard trunk. The outboard sits on a cross beam just inside the transom and the whole trunk is covered-in by a transom lift-up seat. Thus the noise is contained within the well, but unfortunately no noise-absorbing material is fitted on the inside surfaces. Handling is reasonably good. An outdrive can also be fitted. The wheel shelter top folds over onto the cabin roof if desired and vision from the helm is reasonable. The sidedecks are amply wide and there are thoughtfully placed locker tops to step down into the cockpit. The cleats are small. The hull is strongly built (try flexing the sides) but the finish inside and out is a little rough in places and the overall appearance of the cabin leaves something to be desired. There is 5 ft 10 in headroom, a galley and toilet compartment to port, a wardrobe and a pull-out double berth to starboard, and two vee berths in the bows. There are also 25 ft, 27 ft, 30 ft and 38 ft versions. Length overall—22 ft; length waterline approx.—19 ft 6 in; beam—6 ft 10 in; displacement—1·1 tons plus engine. Builders—Dawncraft Cruisers, The Paddock, Kinver, Staffs.

Similar cruisers built solely for canal or river cruising include the Burland 26. The hull is a shallow vee type but with a long deep keel (12 in maximum). Hull lay-up is 11 oz with 5 oz on the deck and superstructure. Several rubbing strakes are fitted. The accommodation layout is similar to the Dawncraft but well finished and incorporates a dinette. Builders—Stone Boat Building Co, Ltd, Newcastle Road, Stone, Staffordshire.

The Dobson 24 (Plate 26) can have either an aft or centre cockpit, the latter also with a Yanmar diesel installed under the cockpit sole. This gives the advantages of an inboard and

26 *Dobson 24* ***Courtesy of*** Practical Boat Owner

27 *Nauticus 27*
Courtesy of Ladyline
Group

two separate living spaces. Dobson Yacht and Boatbuilders, Shardlow, Derby.

Other similar craft are the Nauticus 22 and 27 (Plate 27), Buckingham 20 and 25, and Charnwood 25. All these have GRP shallow vee hulls and are normally outboard driven.

For canal cruising one needs a box-shaped hull to give the maximum space and stability, no flare on the bows, a strong hull skin (10 oz lay up is a good thickness) rubbing strakes and a long, deep keel if the hull is very shallow. To be able to pass under bridges on the English narrow canals the height above the water must be restricted, while the beam must not be more than 6 ft 10 in for entry to locks.

Trentcraft 25

This is a really sensibly laid-out inland GRP family cruiser (Plate 28 and Figure 76). The forward cockpit gives seated passengers a good view forward away from the noise of the engine. A sliding roof and side curtains enclose the cockpit in bad weather and turn the cockpit into another cabin at night. A seated steering position which is designed for comfort is a notable feature. Steering from so far forward takes a little practice to master but there are large transom corner fenders and one looks aft either by standing up or looking along the side; a flagstaff directly in front of the helmsman would help. There is a keel which tapers deeper aft to about 9 inches. The GRP mouldings seem well done—the lay-up is 10 oz on the hull and 6 oz on the cabin sides and deck. The roof is a polyurethane sandwich which is an excellent insulator. The keel is part of the hull moulding and is fitted with concrete ballast. Deck fittings are small but the side decks are reasonably wide and access to the engine is via a door at the aft end of the cabin. An outboard of 10–15 h.p. is sufficient or a 12 h.p. Yanmar diesel outdrive can be fitted, but this adds to the price. In the cabin there is full headroom and the toilet compartment is generous in size. The floor is covered with vinyl, and easily-cleaned Melamine surfaces are evident, but this means that the overall impression of the cabin is not particularly warm and homely. For canal work a lower rubbing strake is fitted and the slab-sided hull and full bows with little flare are eminently suitable. Length overall—

25 ft; length waterline approx.—23 ft; beam—6 ft 10 in; draft—
1 ft 6 in; displacement—1·6 tons plus engine. Builders—
Davison Bros, Ltd, Sawley Bridge Marina, Long Eaton,
Nottingham.

28   Trentcraft 25   Courtesy of Davidson Brothers Ltd

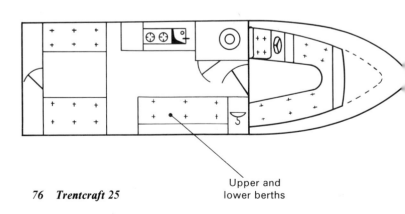

76   Trentcraft 25

Upper and
lower berths

29 *Harborough 42 Courtesy of Harborough Marine Ltd*

Harborough Marine steel canal cruiser

These boats are one of the best examples of the modern steel canal cruiser built to traditional lines (Plate 29). Versions are available from 26 ft to 56 ft long, all with identical cross section, 6 ft 10 in beam and 1 ft 9 in draft. The cross section is rectangular with no keels, so for every foot of boat 0·3 tons of water is displaced. To trim the boat down to this deep draft a large amount of paving stone ballast is fitted in the bilge. A 40 footer weighs about 10 tons and the deep draft gives 6 ft 1 in headroom in the cabin, extremely good stability and complete insensitivity to strong winds. Lister air-cooled diesels are usually fitted (slow running single or twin cylinder engines) of 10–20 h.p. The large propeller and rudder together with tiller steering give excellent control—slow and predictable. The helmsman stands up at the long tiller and the engine controls are put on a pedestal. The engine fits underneath the cockpit sole. A forward cockpit enables passengers to get away from the noise of the engine. The hull is all-welded using $\frac{3}{16}$ in plate on the sides and $\frac{1}{4}$ in on the bottom. The cabin is constructed of GRP. Fitting-out in the cabin is to a high standard with domestic-sized galley equipment. The boats are comfortable enough to live aboard for long periods (Figure 77). They are painted in traditional canal style with black hulls and decorated with castles and roses. Builders—Harborough Marine Ltd, Leicester Road, Market Harborough, Leics.

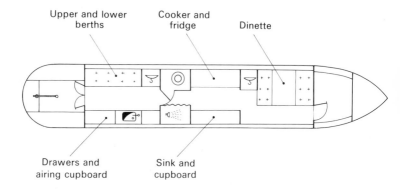

Upper and lower berths   Cooker and fridge   Dinette

Drawers and airing cupboard   Sink and cupboard

77   Harborough Marine 42

There are many other companies building steel canal craft, most supplying part-built as well as complete boats, for example—G. Faulkner (Boatbuilders) Cosgrove, Wolverton, Bucks.; Mindon Marine Ltd, Brookhill Industrial Estate, Station Road, Pinxton, Nottingham; and Springer Engineering Ltd, Mill Hill Road, Market Harborough, Leics.